A breath of heaven

All Saints Convalescent Hospital
Eastbourne, 1869-1959

Kay Syrad

Foreword by Dr. John Elliott

Rosewell Publishing
Rosewell Library
Conquest Hospital
St. Leonards on Sea   TN37 7RD

ISBN: 0-9537901-9-3

We are grateful for permission to use the following photographs:

© Bob Mulvey: Front cover: St. Agnes, detail of Chapel window; St. Clare, p.24; Entrance to Hospital, p.49; Mother's Garden, p.69; St. Peter, p.103; Chapel floor, p.107; & Henry Woodyer Memorial Tablet, p.52 (© Helios Windsor Ltd).
© John Crook, All Saints Chapel, interior, p. 99.
© Nick Taylor, Turreted staircase, p.45; All Saints, south wing, p.57.

© All Saints Sisters of the Poor, Harriet Brownlow Byron, p.13; Scenes of the War in France, p.17.
© Eastbourne County Library Services, All Saints at Meads, p.31; Patronage, p.41; St. Luke's, p.72; All Saints, p.88.
© Dr. Michael Mynott, Laying the Foundation Stone, p.37.
© Martha Walcot, Photographs of the Canadian Military Hospital, pp. 79 & 83.

Printed by Hastings Printing Company Ltd.
Drury Lane, St. Leonards-on-Sea, East Sussex   TN38 9BJ

Contents

Foreword

Today we expect the State to provide a national Health Service: in the nineteenth century things were very different. Religion was central to most aspects of life and, not unnaturally, the church was a provider of health care, especially to those least able to provide for themselves.

Henry Woodyer was an unusual man: a gentleman who lived in style, but also an architect and an avid supporter of the 'high church' faction within the Church of England. Harriet Brownlow Byron was also an unusual woman: born of a respectable and wealthy family she could have decided upon a cosseted life. Instead she chose to join a religious community and to devote herself to the service of others.

All these strands come together at All Saints Convalescent Hospital in Eastbourne: Harriet Brownlow Byron and her followers dispensing loving care within the buildings that Henry Woodyer designed in his very individualistic style.

In this book Kay Syrad describes how the Hospital came to exist and what was done there. She ends her story at a time when the Hospital's future is uncertain. Her words should provide a firm basis for the debate that is now essential as a new use is sought for the Hospital buildings and especially for Woodyer's spectacular Chapel.

Dr. John Elliott
The University of Reading
November 2002

Preface

All Saints Hospital was opened in 1869. The All Saints Sisters of the Poor led by their Mother Superior, Harriet Brownlow Byron, delivered care to the patients with devotion and tenderness. Their philosophy has continued over the years and the principles of care at the Hospital are the same today as they were over a century ago. The only difference today is that the buildings in which the patients are housed are not the modern healthcare facilities that the public has come to expect. The plan for the future, therefore, is to develop services which include caring for patients in their home and providing alternative residential accommodation where the long-held 'Philosophy of Care' will be maintained.

I wanted the history of All Saints Hospital under the management of Harriet Brownlow Byron and her successors to be recorded with the intention of celebrating her vision before the Hospital closes. When this event happens and we move out, future developers will be struck by the grandeur and Gothic architecture of the main Hospital and Chapel. For the sake of maintaining this very strong link with history, the developers will be urged to work sensitively with the building to maintain the beauty of the architecture that was toiled over those many years ago.

Bob Mulvey
General Manager
All Saints Hospital
November 2002

Acknowledgements

The inspiration for this new history of All Saints Convalescent Hospital came from the General Manager of All Saints, Bob Mulvey. Bob provided sustained encouragement and good humour throughout the many months of research and writing, as well as a great deal of practical assistance. Mary Hooper, Curator, Arts in Healthcare, East Sussex Hospital Trust, commissioned and supported the development of the book, and Margaret Richards, Arts in Healthcare, assisted with design and production. Thank you. I am grateful for the financial support provided by East Sussex Hospital Trust and the Friends of Eastbourne Hospitals.

I am also very grateful to Sister Margaret and Dr. Alan Wakely at the Convent of the All Saints Sisters of the Poor at Cowley in Oxford for their generous help during my research in the Convent archives and in their careful reading of a draft version of the book.

I would like to thank a number of others who kindly gave their time and expertise in reading and commenting on early drafts of the book: Canon Denys Giddey, former Chaplain to the Eastbourne Group of Hospitals and author of a previous history of the Hospital; Vera Hodsoll, President of the Eastbourne Local History Society; Penny Jones of Arts in Healthcare at Eastbourne; and John Kimberly, current Chaplain to Eastbourne Hospitals. I am especially indebted to Richard Crook, architect and Victorian specialist, for providing invaluable information about the architecture of the Hospital, and for his close reading of draft versions.

I am grateful, too, to those people who talked to Bob Mulvey and myself about All Saints: Dr. Ian Brown (former Medical Officer to All Saints); Dr. Michael Mynott (formerly visiting GP to All Saints) and Rosalind Mynott; Geraldine Griffiths, All Saints Hospital; Mrs. Martha Walcot in Canada, who generously made a gift to the Hospital of her father's Canadian Military Hospital photograph album; Dr. Jonathan E. Minns, Museum Director, Brighton Engineerium; the Reverend Ray Morrison, former Chaplain to the Hospital; and Rose Bunnett, formerly a member of staff at All Saints, whose memory for details about the Hospital between 1938 and 1958 is astounding.

I would also like to thank Dr. Martin Harrison and Dr. Michael Kerney for kindly helping us to identify the stained glass windows in the chapel; Dr. John Elliott for his Foreword and his helpful comments on the book, and also Dr. John Pritchard, co-author with Dr. John Elliott of the definitive book on All Saints' architect, Henry Woodyer.

Book design by Margaret Richards and Kay Syrad

Introduction

As you approach All Saints Convalescent Hospital, your eye is drawn upwards and your head tips back: you receive chastening notice of your human scale. You cast around for shapes and emblems that you might recognize; your senses take in the textures and colours (bricks made from local clay: red, ochre, orange, plum; black drainpipes with their hopper heads bearing construction dates; cream paintwork; the dark green of a cluster of palm trees, looking, these days, a little embarrassed). You notice the stonework, the variety of patterns in the plate tracery of the windows, the competing angles of the entrance porch roof and the dormer windows. You gaze at a statue, feel puzzled by the narrow turrets at first floor level, and for relief turn away towards the sea light beyond the flint walls. You notice that your tread on the gravel is all you can hear.

You are braced to enter (it requires courage, a small surrender) through what appears to be a low, middle-pointed arch into the porch, through a leaded screen towards an oak door held and manoeuvred by two long iron strap-hinges. You crouch a little (although the height of the doorway is quite adequate), taking in the leaded windows - and unaccountably, a little shame surfaces, unease. You go on through another doorway into an entrance hall whose grandeur is temporarily disguised by pink-ochre paintwork and plain brown carpet. Yet straightaway you know something of the *love* that made possible this phenomenon in the late 1860s: All Saints Convalescent Hospital for the Sick Poor, officially opened in 1869 by Bishop Samuel Wilberforce, the only Bishop in those Protestant days who would 'do anything for the Religious Communities springing up,' on 19th July (St. Vincent de Paul's day), a Monday, the only day he could spare to come and bless the Hospital.

Then, noticing the parade of arched doorways inside, you become aware that the Hospital is more or less a parallelogram, built on an east to west axis, comprising two wings with separate entrances, originally one for men, one for women. Again, despite the presence of a modern lift shaft, your eye is immediately drawn upwards, up one of the two stately stone staircases rising from this central pavilion. You can't help but ascend the staircase, can't help but linger with your hand on the smooth oak balustrade, studying the panels of cast iron cloverleaves designed to stop you falling. You can't help being drawn off the stairs by light beaming along the length of the first floor wards, women's on the right, men's on the left. You move soundlessly towards the tall, decorative windows, again towards the sea light – both east and west. Then back downstairs, through more pointed doorways and into the south wing built for the Sisters' administrative offices and living accommodation. The Sisters: the All Saints Sisters of the Poor, founded in 1851 by Harriet Brownlow Byron, whose handsome face with its wry flicker at the lips, still meets you - confronts you - at the entrance to the Hospital Chapel.

The Sisters: one of the first Church of England sisterhoods since Henry VIII's dissolution of the monasteries in the 1530s, slipping through the middle-pointed doors, coiling up the narrow stairs to the turreted rooms that overlook the wards, moving in silent procession up the oak stairs to the Tribune, looking down on the magnificent Chapel. The rustle of black serge and pale linen as they kneel for prayer, the creak of their starched veils as they rise to sing hymns that had only recently been composed. The Sisters: bringing to Meads at Eastbourne the idea of convalescence on a grand scale for people who may never have breathed sea air, who may never have had a rest or a holiday in their lives (in 1870, the year following the Hospital's opening, more than 1,000 patients benefited from their care, from the sea air, from this great philanthropic idea); bringing to Eastbourne an institution that gave material form to the grandest devotional ideas. All Saints Convalescent Hospital: the only convalescent hospital on such a scale to be managed solely by a religious order; the largest charitable seaside convalescent hospital to be built in Great Britain (and probably the world).

Two of the people who made All Saints Convalescent Hospital possible were Harriet Brownlow Byron and Henry Woodyer, a High Anglican gentleman architect who also designed six Houses of Mercy, two orphanages, part of Eton School, and many substantial churches throughout England. This book, *A Breath of Heaven*, traces how it was that the vision and energy of these two Victorian individuals, together with the astonishing collective labour of hundreds of women and men - in a context of urgent philanthropic concern for the poor, the great Church of England revival, and the dynamic relationship between industry and the arts - combined to create All Saints Convalescent Hospital and its exquisite Chapel – sailing ark-like high above the sea, on land belonging to the Duke of Devonshire in the hamlet of Meads, Eastbourne, between 1867 and the 1880s.

I
Harriet Brownlow Byron
Mother Foundress, All Saints Sisters of the Poor

'There was something so quiet and so strong, so gentle in our dear Mother Foundress, it inspired confidence.'[1]

At the entrance to the Hospital Chapel hangs a magnificent photograph of Harriet Brownlow Byron, founder both of All Saints Convalescent Hospital, Eastbourne, and of the community of the All Saints Sisters of the Poor in 1851 at Margaret Street, St. Marylebone in London. The Mother Foundress, here substantial, imposing, wears a black serge habit and a starched linen scapular that sweeps over her breast and shoulder blades. Round her face rests a close muslin cap with fine pleats, each pleat caught by a thread. Above the muslin, a fiercely starched linen veil sails away from her face, only to bring that face towards us. Her hands are invisible under the folds of the long sleeves. She sits upright. Her intelligence greets us first in the brows, then from under the slightly hooded, crinkled eyelids, in the aquiline nose and in the placing of the modest lips. It is not just intelligence that greets us: there is a palpable integrity in this face; also kindness, and a great stillness.

Harriet Brownlow – called Brownlow or Brownie by her family - was the last of seven children born to Thomas Byron and Louisa Brassey at Bayfordbury, near Hertford, in 1818. Thomas Byron was an MP for Hertford from 1823 until 1830; he was also Deputy Lieutenant of the County of Hertfordshire, and later Lord of the Manor at Coulsdon, Surrey. The family also had a residence in Nottingham Place, Marylebone, where Harriet continued to live after her parents' death until 1851. Harriet's mother, Louisa, an heiress, had a reputation for being extremely kind, sometimes 'sitting up all night to nurse the sick poor.'[2] The family frequently stayed on the European Continent, where Harriet visited convents with her French Roman

---

[1] 'Memories of Sister Caroline Mary,' in Susan Mumm, ed (2001) *All Saints Sisters of the Poor: An Anglican Sisterhood in the Nineteenth Century,* Boydell Press, Church of England Record Society, Vol. 9: 6. Original emphasis. S. Caroline Mary (Caroline Grace Millicent Short) was Mother Superior of All Saints Sisters of the Poor after Harriet's death in 1887 until 1893. These memories were written around 1920, when S. Caroline Mary was in her 80s.
[2] Peter Mayhew (1987) *All Saints: The Birth and Growth of a Community,* Society of All Saints, Oxford: 25. Mayhew was Chaplain to the All Saints Sisters at Oxford 1974-1984.

Catholic governess, becoming particularly fond of two Paris convents of the Sisters of St. Vincent de Paul, whose example was later to influence her own Community.[3]

In 1845, the year her father died, Harriet began to worship at Margaret Chapel in Margaret Street, London, which was then a 'complete paragon of ugliness.'[4] It was demolished in 1850 and replaced by the present church, All Saints, Margaret Street, designed by William Butterfield, and described by George Street (the architect who designed St. Saviour's Church in Eastbourne) as 'not only the most beautiful, but the most vigorous, thoughtful and original of them all.'[5] All Saints was built according to the principles of the Ecclesiological Society,[6] which were that the Church be in the Gothic style of the late thirteenth and fourteenth centuries, that it must be honestly built of solid materials, its ornament should decorate its construction, its 'single, pious and laborious' artist should ponder deeply 'over his duty to do his best for the service of God's Holy Religion,' and the design should be such that the rubrics and canons of the Church of England were observed and the sacraments properly administered.[7] It was the Cambridge Camden Society's model church.

The Ecclesiological Society, a Cambridge-based organisation, tried to give architectural and liturgical expression to the ideas that came out of the Oxford Movement (also known as the Tractarian Movement). In 1833 John Keble, then Professor of Poetry at Oxford, had given a sermon challenging what he saw as the Church's subservience to the State and the alienation of the State from Christian religion. He appealed for 'piety, purity, chastity, and justice' - devotion to 'the cause of the Apostolic Church in these realms.'[8] By 1840 John Henry Newman (later Cardinal Newman) and the Oxford intellectual Dr. Edward Bouverie Pusey were advocating a place for 'Sisters of Mercy' within the Church of England, and Pusey proceeded in 1845 to found the Park Village West Sisters,[9] also in Marylebone — so constituting the formal revival of monasticism within the Church of England. This was a revival of the primacy of the sacraments

---

[3] St. Vincent de Paul was a French priest working in Paris in the 17th century. He founded the first unenclosed order of Sisters of Mercy, who devoted themselves to visiting and nursing the sick and poor.

[4] Mayhew, op.cit: 23.

[5] C.B. Mortlock, ed. (1934) *Famous London Churches*, Skeffington & Son: 156, cited in Mayhew: 30.

[6] Founded as the Cambridge Camden Society in 1839, becoming the Ecclesiological Society in 1845.

[7] Guide to *All Saints, Margaret Street* (1990), Pitkin Pictorials: 4.

[8] John Keble (1847)'The Assize Sermon' in *Sermons*, J.H. Parker: 146-7, cited in Mayhew, op.cit: 1.

[9] Later called the Sisterhood of the Holy Cross.

as a means to salvation and an insistence on active work and charity, both as a form of spiritual discipline and obedience to the demands of Christ.

In fact the very first Protestant sisterhood in England was proposed by Mary Astell in 1696, the 'innocent and holy Souls' of which would measure 'their hours by their Devotions, and their Days by the charitable Works they do.'[10] It was feared, however, that Astell's plan would prepare the way for '*Popish Orders*.' In 1840 Elizabeth Fry, the Quaker philanthropist, set up a non-denominational 'Institution for Nursing Sisters' at Devonshire Square, sometimes referred to as 'Sisters of Charity'; and in 1848, the Sisterhood of Mercy of Devonport and Plymouth was established by a friend of Pusey[11] and members both of this and Pusey's Orders nursed in poor Plymouth homes during the cholera outbreaks of 1848, 1849 and 1853. By 1851 eight Church of England religious communities had been established, each inspired by the principles of the Oxford Movement.

It was in the context of these theological and merciful developments that Harriet Brownlow Byron came under the influence of All Saints' new Minister, William Upton Richards, who trained her for the spiritual life and in particular for district visiting in the Margaret Chapel area, where works of mercy at that time included tending the sick and the poor in their homes, visiting hospitals, workhouses and prisons, helping destitute children, giving shelter to 'distressed women of good character' and assisting in the burial of the dead. Under Upton Richards' tutelage, Harriet studied the early Fathers of the Church, meditated, kept the Canonical Hours and learned to fast. She had to fight against her own strong will and was always trying to be 'still more humble,'[12] both then and throughout her life: over her sitting room door at the Convent in Margaret Street, Harriet kept the motto (in Latin) '*Humility – Humility –Humility*' 'and most earnestly had she made it *the rock* of her life and work. It was *child-like* Humility, so simple, so bright, so true.'[13]

In 1849 Harriet supervised the district poor school in Great Titchfield Street and undertook nurse training at King's College Hospital, an Anglican institution established in 1840 with fifty beds, catering mostly for patients from the slum areas between the Strand and Regent Street,

[10] Mary Astell (1696) *A Serious Proposal to the Ladies for the Advancement of their True and Greatest Interest*, cited in Peter F. Anson (1955) *The Call of the Cloister*, S.P.C.K: 17.

[11] These Sisters later set up a printing works staffed entirely by women.

[12] Mayhew, op.cit: 26.

[13] S. Caroline Mary, in Mumm, op.cit: 36-7. Original emphasis.

and where there was already some effort being made to improve the standard of nursing. There is speculation that because of her social status, Harriet may have received special training by the doctors, and indeed she was later described, regarding her work in the Franco-Prussian war, as an exceptionally well-trained nurse. One of the Sisters described Harriet's caring for the sick in the early days of the Sisterhood in Margaret Street:

'Our Mother Foundress used to undertake the cases, *when there were bad wounds*. There was one poor woman…whose face and hands had terrible wounds and disfigurement from some kind of disease. Our Mother used to let me be her Assistant and hand her the things, *lint* and *ointment*, used to dress the poor woman…Our Mother did all so beautifully with real skill and gentleness. She used her forceps and never her fingers. It took a long time in the morning to do this work of mercy…'[14]

During this year Harriet suffered the first of many periods of illness and her favourite brother died; in the following year her desire to live 'wholly to God' began to deepen. Then in August 1851, Harriet and Upton Richards acquired a house in Mortimer Street (parallel to Margaret Street), and having scrubbed the house with the help of a maid, Harriet took in two sickly orphan girls. She first slept in the house on St. Luke's Day, 18th October 1851, which is the day observed by the All Saints Sisters as their Foundation Day, the day on which Harriet began to live her 'solitary Religious Life.' In December, Sarah Easton came to join Harriet, and the Community was begun, without formal Professions, which did not begin until 1856.

Soon another Mortimer Street house was acquired and added to what had become St. Elizabeth's Hospital, and in 1856 Upton Richards and Harriet took a long lease of three houses across the road from the site of the new All Saints Church in Margaret Street.[15] In May 1856 Harriet, Sarah Easton and another woman, Ellen Wilson, after their long training, were professed as 'Full Choir Sisters.' On the 3rd August 1856, Harriet, now aged thirty-eight, the woman who was to found the grand All Saints Convalescent Hospital at Eastbourne, was elected 'Mother for Life' of the All Saints Society of the Sisters of the Poor. The next day the

---

[14] Ibid: 6.

[15] It appears that over the years several houses in Mortimer Street (2, 3, 80 and 81) and 8 Margaret Street were in fact built especially for the Sisters. They took the form of ordinary houses in case they had to be given up at the end of the Lease. S. Catherine Williams, in Mumm (2001): 53.

Harriet Brownlow Byron, Mother Foundress

Sisters, aged women, incurables, older girls in training (known as 'Industrial Girls'), and orphans, moved into Margaret Street, the new building was blessed, and Harriet, as Mother Superior, was installed by the Bishop of Oxford, Samuel Wilberforce, acting for the Bishop of London.

There they were then: three All Saints Sisters of the Poor caring for a household of women and girls brought there by a great variety of circumstances, the Sisters' arduous work 'held' by their Augustinian Rule, in which community life was 'simply the practice of love.'[16] In the service of this ideal, the Sisters followed a daily programme of rising at 5 or 5.30am, saying Lauds at 6.40am, Holy Communion at 7am, Prayers with the aged women at 7.45am, Family Prayers at 8.15am and Terce at 8.45am.[17] During this time, the aged women were dressed and read to; after Terce was needlework and 'attending to the outdoor poor,' school or district work, and the collection of food. The orphans, with a Sister, used to go to Hotel kitchens and the wealthier houses where they had permission to collect baskets full of scraps. All, including Mother Foundress, ate these scraps, and only at certain meals (no meat, except midday meal; bread and cheese or butter for supper). Mother Foundress went on these missions hoping that she wouldn't bump into any of the young men who had so recently been her dancing partners, for now she wore a simple black dress and a close white 'baby-cap,' living in accordance with a Religious Rule of obedience, poverty, silence and self-sacrifice.[18]

Sext was at noon, then rest, dinner at 12.30pm, recreation, during which the orphans were taken for a walk, None at 3pm; after None, the Sisters again read to the aged women, worked with the orphans and engaged in school and district work. There was further recreation at 4.15 and Evensong or Vespers, then supper at 6pm, followed by another recreation and yet more work and prayer. The Sisters' working day ended at 8.15pm with 'Spiritual Reading or Private Devotion,' Compline at 9pm and bed at 10pm. One Sister described the atmosphere of the Sisters' houses as 'so quiet and yet so bright…one Sister was with a few Industrial Girls in the yard and they were singing, as they walked up and down, so *happily*.'[19]

---

[16] Mayhew, op.cit: 40

[17] Lauds (or Prime), Terce, Sext, None, Vespers and Compline are the services (Hours) in the Divine Office of the Christian Church, traditionally said or chanted at, respectively, daybreak, the third hour (9am), the 6th hour (noon), the ninth hour (3pm), evening, and before retiring for the night.

[18] Mayhew, op.cit: 29.

[19] S. Caroline Mary, in Mumm (2001): 4.

Even within this ordered and prayerful regime, Mother Foundress encouraged the Sisters to put work before their devotions: '…we old (first) sisters were trained for <u>work</u> and not for the religious life…Mother Superior was always saying <u>Work</u> and pray – or, that work must come first, and Meditations, Devotions, etc. must make way if the work came.'[20] The Sisterhoods considered that no work was intrinsically degrading: indeed, to Anglican Sisters the Victorian horror at ladies doing servants' work was an 'irrational and irreligious idea.' The Rule of a similar Sisterhood, the Holy Rood Community, reminded its Sisters that 'all must work at least as hard as women who work for their daily bread,'[21] and live a life similar to that of the poor. In fact, many Sisters (who, like Harriet Brownlow, were educated women and wealthy in their own right) actually enjoyed the contrast between their former affluent lifestyles and their chosen lives of poverty. One All Saints district visitor, Sister Margaret, who had brought a fortune of diamonds into the Community, also brought vermin back from her daily visits in a slum district, and Sister Rosamund, a wealthy and talented artist when she joined the All Saints Sisters, was in charge of Manchester Workhouse's Infirmary from 1866-1877 where she insisted on living in a workhouse cell identical to those inhabited by the paupers.[22] It was Sister Rosamund who painted the gold cloverleaves on the balustrades of the stairs at All Saints Convalescent Hospital, and who also wrote the religious texts above the doorways to the wards and the Sisters' rooms.

However, unlike most working women, the Sisters were given one month's rest each year to visit families or travel, and a monthly retreat day. European tours were very popular and often undertaken by small groups of Sisters from one or more Communities. Daily recreation was, however, timetabled as strictly as work, as can be seen from the daily programme above: one or two recreational periods per day, to be used for writing letters, needlework, chess, music and reading. Discussion of work was forbidden during recreation, enabling the All Saints Sisters to discuss, for example, Italian politics.[23] This choice of subject was not random: the Crimean War (1854-6) heralded the beginning not only of changes in medical and nursing practice, but also a change in public perceptions of, and philanthropic involvement in, military action. Three

---

[20] Sister Elspeth's 'History of the Community,' ibid: 188.

[21] Susan Mumm (1999): *Stolen Daughters, Virgin Mothers: Anglican Sisterhoods in Victorian Britain,* Leicester University Press: 67.

[22] Ibid: 96. See also Susan Mumm (2001) *Headlice and Diamonds: The Birth of the Sisterhoods,* a Lecture given on 3rd November 2001 at All Saints Margaret Street, London W1, to the Anglo-Catholic History Society.

[23] Ibid: 70.

Anglican Sisters published memoirs of their time in the Crimea and in 1856 Catherine Marsh had published her bestseller idealizing the English officer, appealing to an increasing adulation for the military (known as 'scarlet fever'). Later there was a great deal of support amongst liberal-minded women for the cause of Garibaldi and Italian unification, partly inspired by the poet Elizabeth Barrett Browning and the artist Barbara Leigh Smith[24] who organized medical aid for Garibaldi's troops. By the end of the Franco-Prussian war, to which eight All Saints Sisters travelled in 1870, including Mother Foundress, the relationship between soldiers and civilians was completely transformed, giving women in particular, as nurses, fundraisers and committee organizers, new access to and interest in the political process.[25] Thus the All Saints Sisters spent their recreation discussing Italian politics.

As the Community grew, the All Saints Sisterhood developed a hierarchy comprising Choir Sisters, Lay Sisters and Novices. The Choir Sisters generally came from upper or middle-class backgrounds, with 35% from clergy families. As women were barred at that time from political and legal work 'some of them saw in sisterhoods the possibility of exercising authority and fulfilling their ambitions in an alternative sphere.'[26] Their average age at profession was about thirty-three, after two years' novitiate. Lay Sisters usually came from the upper working-class, with fathers who were farmers, artisans, small tradesmen or shopkeepers, women who may previously have been domestic servants, or sometimes infant school mistresses or ward nurses in hospitals. Lay Sisters entered at the younger average age of twenty-six, candidates usually having had strong ties to the Community, and for whom training in domestic or nursing duties was seen as more important than a sound theological education. They were restricted from holding high office, dressed in easily-washed dark blue cotton instead of black serge, and were urged to 'strive against their carnal wills' in a Rule not deemed necessary for the Choir Sisters. These Sisters were helped by a substantial number of Outer Sisters who followed a simple Rule and wore a plain black dress and bonnet whilst working within the Sisters' Houses. The ratio of Outer Sisters to professed Sisters may have been as much as 10:1. All these Sisters were part of

[24] Later Madame Bodichon, Barrett Browning's cousin.
[25] Anne Summers (1988) *Angels and Citizens: British Women as Military Nurses 1854-1914*, Routledge& Kegan Paul: 125-7.
[26] Ibid: 37.

Scenes of the War in France, 1870
The English Ambulance in the Field, showing All Saints Sisters

a 'Religious Community [which aimed] at the perfection of a life hidden with God in devotion and charity.'[27]

Because the All Saints Sisters of the Poor were a fashionable community, drawn from well-educated women with high social status, the daughter of a minor official here might be a Lay Sister, whereas elsewhere she might be a Choir Sister. Maria Francesca Rossetti (sister of poet Christina and artist Dante Gabriel Rossetti) was a Choir Sister at All Saints, devoting herself to

---

[27] From 'Rules for Outer Sisters 1894,' reprinted in Mumm (2001).

the translation of the Day Hours of the Church from Latin into English (the Community used her translation into the twentieth century).[28] Many sisters from All Saints and the other Communities made translations from the Latin – an important and valued skill, as early Communities needed information on the religious life that was hitherto only available in this form.

In fact, the story of Maria Francesca Rossetti gives us further insight into the Sisters' lives. Maria was seriously ill in 1873, first with erysipelas[29] and then with cancer, and it was at this time that she decided to move from being an Outer Sister to join All Saints as a Novice. This news appalled Maria's brother Dante Gabriel, not least because of what he perceived as the discomfort of convent life. He wrote to his younger brother William: 'I have really felt very seriously anxious about Maria since what you tell me of no fires in this blessed place. I simply could not exist on such terms – it would be a noviciate for another world; and I view the matter as most serious for her.'[30] Christina Rossetti, however, approved of her sister's decision. According to her biographer, Georgina Battiscombe, Christina Rossetti was an Outer Sister of All Saints herself, working at the All Saints 'House of Charity,' and nuns were the subjects of several of her famous poems.[31] William also understood that his eldest sister had a genuine vocation: 'Of all the people I have known, Maria was the most naturally and ardently devotional – certainly more so than Christina, as a matter of innate tendency.'[32] Similarly, Maria is described by Mother Foundress's successor, Sister Caroline Mary, as

'not only deeply spiritual, but also highly educated and a thorough Italian. She used to make her Confession weekly, and had a great gift of '*tears.*' She often wept in Prayer when in Chapel. Being very learned in Scripture, I deputed her to give Bible lessons to some of the very young Novices…Our Mother Foundress often saw Sister Maria Francesca, as she knew and understood her soul well and could help her in her scruples and difficulties more than I could.

---

[28]Summers, op.cit: 73. Maria Rossetti was herself a convalescent at All Saints Convalescent Hospital in Eastbourne in 1874 and again in 1876.

[29] Erysipelas, a common disease of this period, is a skin disease caused by streptococcus.

[30] Cited in Georgina Battiscombe (1981) *Christina Rossetti, A Divided Life*, Constable: 153.

[31] Christina Rossetti's name does not appear, however, in the All Saints book which lists all the Outer Sisters from the beginning of the Community.

[32] Ibid: 154. Another poet's sister (and a poet in her own right) who joined the All Saints Sisters was Milicent Hopkins, sister of the famous Jesuit priest Gerard Manley Hopkins.

Mother Foundress also gave her the work of translating a Latin Breviary; and our Office book.'[33]

Perhaps Dante Gabriel Rossetti also knew something of the spirit of self-abnegation which existed in the early Sisterhoods, mainly inspired by Pusey's insistence that the self should die so that Christ could enter one's soul. Fortunately both Reverend Upton Richards and Mother Foundress were humane and psychologically sensitive enough to recognize and attend to the Sisters' individual strengths and weaknesses, but when Mother Foundress's beloved co-founder died in 1873, she and the Sisterhood embraced the chaplaincy of the extreme Pusey-ite Father Benson of the Society of St. John the Evangelist (S.S.J.E.)[34] in which the Sisters were encouraged to detach themselves from the world by ignoring and crushing their human emotions. It was this emphasis on self-mortification that so distressed Karen Armstrong when she joined a Roman Catholic sisterhood in 1962, when it was still working on Victorian principles.[35]

Nevertheless, it remained possible for the Sisters to make the necessary sacrifices with grace and love. A contemporary and something of a sceptic, Dinah Mulock Craik, described the Anglican Sisters thus:

'Gradually the whole Chapel became filled with Sisters, who I saw were divided into three classes – the black-veiled, the white-veiled, and the novices…in their plain black gowns and white or black veils of some soft-falling, close-fitting material – a costume as becoming and comfortable as any woman can wear. It seemed to suit all the faces, young and old, and some were quite elderly and not over beautiful; but every one had that peculiar expression of mingled sweetness and peace…'[36]

Not everyone held a benign view of the Sisters in the 1850s, however. One of the All Saints Sisters recalled 'Much suspicion & 'ill' was thought of them & the *dress* of 'a Sister' disliked and

[33] 'Memories of Sister Caroline Mary,' in Mumm (2001): 25.
[34] Richard Meux Benson, of the S.S.J.E., which was one of the earliest monastic communities for men in the post-Reformation Church of England.
[35] See Karen Armstrong (1981/1994) *Through the Narrow Gate*, St. Martin's Press, New York.
[36] Dinah Mulock Craik (c.1858) 'On Sisterhoods' reprinted in Elaine Showalter, ed (1993), *Maude, On Sisterhoods, A Woman's Thoughts about Women*, William Pickering: 49.

scoffed at. When at length I received 'the Habit'…passers by often scoffed or showed positive hatred of our outside dress –' made faces' at us & called us 'Sisters of Misery' (sic) and one's own relations even 'pitied us.'[37]

The Sisters suffered not only this casual and local animosity, but also the fury of members of the Church of England itself. Many in the Church of England disliked the ritualistic practices of these religious communities; the ritualists were described as 'a very serious evil' capable of 'bringing the clergy into contempt,'[38] and in the late 1860s, at the time the Convalescent Hospital at Eastbourne was being set up, All Saints Church at Margaret Street experienced frequent and notorious arguments between ritualistic clergy and dismayed patrons and parishioners.[39] Nevertheless, eighty women were professed into the All Saints Sisters of the Poor between 1851 and 1876, despite that other site of resistance, their own families, many of whom forbade their daughters to enter the Sisterhoods. Some women were unable to resolve the conflict between their familial duties and their yearning for the Sisterhood, and instead supported the Communities financially and as Outer Sisters. A large portion of the cost of the Chapel at All Saints Convalescent Hospital was the gift of a woman who had given up her ambition to join the community because she felt it was her duty to be a mother to her brother's children.

The Sisterhoods were an important innovator in that they gave women the freedom to work in the non-domestic sphere, without waiting for outside permission, supervision or even approval. Moreover, it was said that '…entering a Sisterhood, almost any sort of Sisterhood where there was work to do, authority to compel the doing of it, and companionship to sweeten the same, would have saved many a woman from the lunatic asylum.'[40] Extreme though this

---

[37] Sister Catherine Williams, 'The recollections of an old woman, November 1907,' in Mumm (2001): 52. Original emphasis. S. Catherine was an All Saints Sister from 1870-1917.

[38] Cited in Stanley Meacham (1970) *Lord Bishop: The Life of Samuel Wilberforce 1805-1873*, Harvard University Press, Cambridge, Mass.: 260.

[39] The fear of losing Church of England members to Rome was not entirely unjustified. Newman had left the Oxford Movement for the Roman Catholic Church; of the 21% of the All Saints Sisters who left the Community, more than 36% joined Roman Catholic Communities. (See Mumm, 2001) Once when she was abroad Harriet wrote to Upton Richards to say that she felt attracted to the Roman Catholic Church: he called her straight back to London. Years later in Siena, one the Sisters remarked to Mother how near they were to Rome. Mother smiled; they did not go to Rome. (See Mayhew, op.cit).

[40] Craik, op.cit: 55.

may sound, many middle and upper-middle class women in the early and mid-Victorian period were obliged to lead claustrophobic, eventless and soul-numbing lives. One of the most vociferous writers on this subject was none other than Florence Nightingale: in her novel *Cassandra* (c.1850) her character demands on women's behalf not money or votes or even work, but the restoration of pain:

'Give us back our suffering, we cry to heaven in our hearts – suffering rather than indifferentism; for out of nothing comes nothing. But out of suffering may come the cure. Better have pain than paralysis! ...rather, ten times rather, die in the surf, heralding the way to that new world, than stand idly on the shore!'[41]

'Sickness, and crime, and poverty in masses' were, Nightingale argued, the antidotes to the mental paralysis in women's lives. Women took heed: by the end of the century there were at least ninety Sisterhoods involving the full time labour of almost ten thousand women. These Sisters not only cared quietly for the aged or for orphans, they also preached in their chapels, fundraised, built and managed the finances of convents, hospitals, orphanages, schools, took positions of authority and responsibility within the larger community, wrote books, lobbied MPs, presented petitions to Parliament, founded Communities in every continent in the world, and took pride in their influence and achievements, which were 'all within a completely female authority structure.'[42] They also gradually commanded respect, not least because of their patriotic nursing work for the military in the European campaigns of the second half of the century: Florence Nightingale's first party to arrive in the Crimea in 1856 comprised eight Sisters and six nurses from Anglican Orders, ten Catholic Sisters of Mercy and fourteen secular nurses; the Emperor of Germany sent an Iron Cross for the Mother and Sisters of All Saints as an acknowledgement of their services in the Franco-Prussian war.[43]

Mother's work as Foundress was much harder after the death of Reverend Upton Richards, and her respectful silence regarding the strictness of Father Benson's chaplaincy concealed painful alterations to the Sisters' practice. For example, Father Benson decided to cut some of

---

[41] Cited in Elaine Showalter (1987) *The Female Malady: Women, Madness and English Culture, 1830-1980*, Virago: 65.
[42] Mumm (1999): 210.
[43] The Iron Cross is no longer in the possession of the All Saints Sisters, however. There is speculation that it may have been melted down for munitions during World War I.

the Saints from the Community's new Office book, including St. Frances de Sales, some of whose convents Mother Foundress knew and loved, the great mystic St. John of the Cross, and her favourite saint, St. Vincent de Paul. Mother Foundress was also weakened by serious illness at this time: she suffered spinal cancer, and later contracted breast cancer. The end approached, despite operations and being tended by the best physicians, and Harriet Brownlow Byron died on 3rd August 1887. 'The last day we [the Sisters] went into her room whenever we could & knelt by her bedside. S. Eliza stood at the foot like a statue & put eau de Cologne on Mother's feet sometimes…'[44]

Mother Foundress was at last laid in her coffin and 'covered with the choisest [sic] flowers the loving offering of many…both rich & poor were allowed to come for a last look of her they had so loved & revered.'[45] The funeral service for the late Reverend Mother was conducted by Archbishop Edward White Benson and a Requiem celebration of the Eucharist was held in All Saints, Margaret Street, attended by members of many religious communities and one hundred and twenty five All Saints Sisters. Sister Caroline Mary was elected as the second Mother Superior. Mother Foundress is buried a few feet away from her spiritual mentor and friend, Reverend Upton Richards, in Brompton Cemetery, west London.

One can begin to see, then, the context in which Mother Foundress worked and prayed, and that to manage a pioneering Sisterhood she would need, at the very least, enormous strength and courage. She was also what one might these days call a 'social entrepreneur,' that is, someone who is good at 'detecting gaps in the social fabric and creating a commonwealth of opportunity.'[46] An example of this ability, and one of Mother Foundress's great achievements, was in providing *all* the nursing for University College Hospital between 1862 and 1898.

---

[44] S. Catherine Williams, in Mumm (2000): 64.
[45] Ibid.
[46] This is Michael Young's definition in A. Briggs (2001), *Michael Young: Social Entrepreneur*, Palgrave, cited by Peter Lucas in *The Local Historian*, (2001) Vol. 32, No.2: 90.

II
The All Saints Sisters at
University College Hospital

Nursing was the essential, primary work of the All Saints Sisters, as it was for all the Anglican and Catholic sisterhoods of the period. In the early nineteenth century there were in fact a wide variety of medical, religious and philanthropic movements relating to the care and cure of the sick. The needs of the majority were met by the public authorities under the Poor Law, usually through 'outdoor relief,' which meant receiving medical attention in their own homes. For those needing 'indoor relief' there were voluntary hospitals, providing for only a minority of the sick poor, excluding cases such as cancer, scurvy, consumption and smallpox. Other patients were tended in infirmaries within the workhouses and those with contagious diseases were sent to borough isolation hospitals.

In none of these institutions were nurses expected to have any particular training or qualification for the work, and, caricatured in Dickens' characters Sarah Gamp and Betsy Prig, were allegedly women 'of inadequate skill, coarse manners, low character and bibulous tendencies.'[47] During the same period, men did all the army nursing, were often employed in the expanding number of mental institutions (chiefly for the purpose of control and restraint), and in civilian hospitals some skilled nursing work was carried out by male medical students or junior medical officers (known as 'dressers' or 'clinical clerks').

During the 1840s a number of workhouse and asylum scandals and tragedies, together with a high incidence of typhus and consumption amongst the overcrowded poorer classes, plus periodic outbreaks of smallpox and cholera, combined to bring the problems of the sick poor to the attention of medical observers and upper and middle-class enthusiasts for sanitary reform. In 1849 physician Edward Sieveking found that many workhouses were already allowing some 'trustworthy inmates' to go as nurses to the neighbouring poor and he had the idea of turning the Poor Law infirmaries into training institutions for nurses. It was however

---

[47] F.J.C. Hearnshaw (1929) *The Centenary History of King's College Hospital, London, 1828-1928*, London: 231, cited in S.W.F. Holloway, 'The All Saints Sisterhood at University College Hospital, 1862-1899,' in *Medical History* (1959), Vol. III: 148.

St. Clare: window in All Saints Chapel

the voluntary hospitals in which eventually the two-tier arrangement of nursing preferred by Florence Nightingale was strengthened so that domestic work was clearly demarcated from the management of nurses. This division was highly significant to the upper and middle-class women coming into nursing, religious or secular, as it was work with which they were familiar in their own homes: the management of domestic staff.

The efficacy of nursing was also becoming significant in relation to the development of specialised medical and surgical treatment and the concomitant expansion of the teaching function of hospitals. Surgeons and physicians were anxious that patients recovering from surgery or receiving new treatments were constantly watched over and given the correct medicines or external applications. In 1857 this new appreciation of nursing was articulated by the Senior Surgeon at St. Thomas' Hospital thus: '…only those who have operated…know how greatly the success of operations depends on good nursing.'[48]

A fuller explanation for the emergence of the Christian nursing Sisterhoods at this particular time lies, then, in the combination of embryonic developments in medicine and nursing practice itself and the frustrations of upper and middle-class women, at a time when both rural and urban poverty had reached a crisis after a series of bad harvests, and before the failure of the Chartists' Third Petition removed the fear of a working-class insurrection. For the first time, the divide between 'the two nations' (rich and poor) had become a subject for anxious *moral* and political consideration. Moreover,

'The necessities of our helpless poor, and a consciousness of the increased power obtained from combination…have led to the idea of working together in a body. Hence societies are formed…*The need of doing the work has led to developing the life; not the life looking abroad for a work to which to attach itself.*'[49]

Charity was seen as 'a precious medium of conciliation and communication. It was also a medium for the teaching of Christianity…The state of medical knowledge…was not such that the sufferer could be assured of recovery. The sickbed might be the last place where the soul could be brought to recognise the necessity and the source of salvation, and be rescued from

---

[48] J.F. South (1857), *Facts relating to Hospital Nurses*, London: 11, cited in Summers, op.cit: 16.
[49] T.T. Carter (1853), *Objections to Sisterhoods Considered, in a Letter to a Parent,* F. & J. Rivington: 18, cited in Mumm (2001): 17.

the pains of hell. Care of the body was not ignored, but its prime importance lay in facilitating the cure of the soul.'[50]

The truth of this assertion is borne out by the first statement in the All Saints Sisters' 1855 *Rules and Admonitions:* 'The primary object of this Society is to provide a *religious* Asylum for incurables, aged and infirm persons in destitute circumstances, and to train up Orphan children to useful employments; and although other works of mercy may from time to time be added at the discretion of the Superiors, these shall always have the first consideration and hold the principal place in the work of the Sisters.'[51]

In 1848 the St. John's House Training Institution for Nurses was founded by an Anglican group that included the Bishop of London, the Reverend Frederick Dennison Maurice (former Chaplain of Guy's Hospital), and William Gladstone, MP. This was the first Sisterhood within the Church of England to be designed exclusively as a nursing order, and it played a particularly important role in the Crimean expedition. Although established to provide home nursing for the poor, it was also seen as a 'potential vehicle for the reform of hospital nursing – by providing a better quality nurse for hospital work.'[52] It was understood that this was about spiritual rather than medical improvement, even though members of St. John's did not take religious vows. However, in the bid for this type of improvement, St. John's worked within a structure that was to provide the basis for all subsequent nurse training (including that of Florence Nightingale). The hierarchy comprised Sisters, probationers and nurses, and Associate Sisters. The Sisters accepted no salary and paid for their own board; they trained and supervised the probationers, and visited the sick and poor in their own homes. The probationers and nurses received wages, were trained for private and hospital work and assisted with domestic work.

The non-payment of the Sisters was the source of years of conflict in the history of nurse training. The system emulated that of the upper or middle-class women's domestic situation: that is, responsibility for the organisation and management of staff, but without pay. Thus many such women were attracted to nursing, and were suited to its management. For those who favoured this system, it also indicated the 'disinterested and spiritual character of her work, and

---

[50] Summers, op.cit: 18.
[51] 'The Rules of 1855' reprinted in Mumm (2001): 67.
[52] Summers, op.cit: 20.

her fitness to exercise authority.'[53] Thus the notions of social and spiritual superiority were conflated:

'women of means were automatically assumed to be more spiritually endowed than working women, and were also deemed qualified to instruct the latter in the proper duties of a hospital and private nurse, without themselves having to undergo any practical probation...It was worth asking – as Florence Nightingale was to ask, in exasperation, many times in the 1850s and 1860s, why a group of women of independent income and religious inclination, but without formal training of any kind, should have been considered competent to perform these functions.'[54]

Meanwhile Florence Nightingale continued to insist that nursing was an aid to the prevention and cure of disease, not a means to save souls. She considered the laws of health the laws of God: 'to reveal and follow them was to do His will. Caring for the sick was an act of self-sacrifice and charity which was not to be exploited in any competition between sects or creeds.'[55] There was competition of course, and after Florence Nightingale's and the Sisterhoods' work in the Crimea, which did much to establish both the need for proper nurse training and to enhance the status and acceptability of the Anglican Sisterhoods, both sectarian and non-sectarian groups competed for recognition by Hospital governors and the charitable public.

It was only after three years of pursuing what one historian has described as 'an unremitting policy of infiltration' into University College Hospital that the All Saints Sisters of the Poor were invited in 1862 to be responsible for its entire nursing requirements at this 'godless' hospital in London;[56] and this was apparently to ensure that the All Saints Sisters were not

---

[53] Ibid: 22.

[54] In a letter to Col. Clark Kennedy in 1861, Nightingale objected to 'making it a test of a person's devotion to any service that he or she will perform it gratuitously.' Cited in Summers, op.cit: 300.

[55] Ibid: 23.

[56] Up to the 1820s a university education was only available to members of the Church of England (Oxford and Cambridge) or Presbyterians in Scotland. UCH opened in 1828 both as a College and a hospital where students could gain clinical practice. See also Bernard Lucas (1983) 'The Godless Hospital,' in *UCH 1833-1983*.

totally overshadowed by St. John's House which in 1856 had taken over the entire nursing of King's College Hospital.[57]

This alleged 'unremitting policy of infiltration' actually consisted of Mother Foundress sending a letter in December 1859 to the UCH Board of Governors requesting permission for two of the Sisters to attend the Hospital daily 'for the purpose of learning how to nurse the sick and dress wounds.' Neither the surgeons nor the Matron objected to this and Mother Foundress gave an assurance that there would be no interference with the religious views of patients. When the Head Nurse of two of the wards resigned, Mother Foundress immediately offered the service of a 'Lady Nurse and assistances from All Saints House' for these wards, saying that she and her nurses would be quite willing to comply with the rules and to consider themselves under the control of the Matron of the Hospital.

Then in September 1861 the Kentish Town railway disaster severely strained the Hospital's resources but provided a fine opportunity for the All Saints Sisters to show again that they could supply extra nurses at short notice. Major railway accidents were not very common, but outbreaks of smallpox, typhoid and cholera were: between 1865-6 there was a smallpox epidemic, then in the mid-summer of 1866, Asiatic cholera struck east London, with 230 cases in the first two weeks and forty patients dying every night.[58] In the All Saints House a reserve of nurses was always available. Thus the association grew - perhaps helped by the fact that Sir William Jenner, one of UCH's eminent physicians, was also Mother Foundress's (and the Rossetti family's) private doctor - until, by an Agreement of 23rd April 1862 'the entire arrangements of the Hospital as far as they apply to the nurses and female servants, of the establishment [were] committed to the charge of All Saints House.'[59]

The new All Saints staff consisted of a Head Sister who acted as 'Lady Superintendent' of the Hospital, one Head Nurse to each pair of the seven wards, two nurses to each main ward and one housekeeper. A staff of women servants was also provided with sufficient assistance to perform all the 'scrubbing' throughout the Hospital. The Hospital Committee paid £1,000 annually to All Saints but was refunded the cost of board of the Sisters, nurses and servants; this figure soon turned out to be far too little. The nursing staff operated outside the immediate control of the Hospital Committee and was directly responsible through the Lady

---

[57] Holloway, op.cit: 146-7.
[58] Mumm (2001): 56.
[59] W.R. Merrington (1976) *University College Hospital and its Medical School: a history*, Heinemann: 251.

Superintendent to the Mother Superior, with the Head Sister making a fortnightly report to the Committee. It was exactly the system of which Florence Nightingale so disapproved:

'If a religious head of a religious order has undivided authority over a hospital it will be badly nursed. If a medical staff has individual authority over hospital nursing the hospital will be badly nursed. Otherwise it matters not whether the nurses are lay-women, Anglican or any other 'sisters,' nuns or what not, the essential thing is that they be trained good Nurses, who will not allow any scruples, religious or unreligious to interfere with the faithful discharge. I put the religious scruples of Sisters, neglecting their duty for their devotions, on a par with the unreligious scruples of nurses neglecting their duty for their drink. It has nothing to do at all with such questions as to whether nursing be a 'Church Duty' or not. Nor as to whether it is well or ill to have 'sisterhoods' with all their 'repented evils.'[60]

Repented evils or none, the lives of the Sisters working in University College Hospital were extremely arduous. The nurses' accommodation was 'small and gloomy' with 'unfit sanitary arrangements.'[61] Sister Cecilia wrote in 1886 that 'The women in the laundry find it impossible to get through the amount of washing...and the result is that much of the body linen remains in bins for two or three weeks or longer...gets rotten and is also frequently gnawed by rats...' Another, Sister Harriet Jodison, recalled having to wash soiled linen in a poorly lit basement cellar, with little plumbing or ventilation, a situation over which she wept many tears.[62] One Sister had to ask, in 1885, 'would it be possible for some other arrangement to be made...for removing the dead...The present plan of using a basket is repugnant to the feelings of patients...'

There were many outbreaks of serious illness among nurses in these unhygienic conditions in spite of sustained and conscientious efforts by the Sisters to improve the care of patients, the running of the wards and the welfare of the nursing staff. Ignorance of the nature and avenues of infection was clearly responsible for much disease: in 1880 the Hospital Secretary called the Sister Superior's attention to the fact that dirty linen was being thrown down the food lift. In

[60] From a letter from Nightingale to Harry Bonham Carter, 1866, cited in C. Rivett-Carnac, 'Looking back' in *UCH Nurses' League Magazine*, Jubilee Edition (1959): 25.
[61] Merrington, op.cit: 253.
[62] Ibid.

1871 there were eleven deaths from pyaemia, one from septicaemia, five from erysipelas and one from tetanus.[63] In 1880, one of the Sisters died from diptheria contracted in the Hospital; in 1886 a UCH nurse died of typhoid fever and a patient who had been sent to Eastbourne to convalesce had developed typhoid from which she died.[64]

One of the problems with the Sisterhood's management of the nursing was that its main concern was to train their own Probationers, who were then immediately drafted away to private and district nursing, leaving a residue of inexperienced nurses. This was cited as one of the reasons given for terminating the Sisters' contract in 1899, the other reasons being the revolution in medical training and nursing methods and the Sisters' alleged reluctance to abandon old practices or to employ new knowledge, especially concerning infection. There was also the matter of the Sisters' clothes: it wasn't until 1898 that they agreed to wear white dresses instead of their habits, and at first agreed to change of dress only in the operating theatre. They were also charged with failing to keep the Hospital expenditure within reasonable limits: debts incurred included a £600 butcher's bill. The Sisters resigned in October 1898 but stayed until July 1899.

By the 1880s most Sisterhoods were in fact 'placing less emphasis on nursing as it became a respectable secular profession and the quality and quantity of non-sisterhood nurses improved…the emphasis moved towards patient care in [the Sisterhoods'] own specialist hospitals, usually for convalescents or children, areas where they felt provision was still inadequate.'[65]

---

[63] Ibid. Pyaemia is blood poisoning with fever, common in cases where bones have been injured or following amputation.
[64] Ibid: 254.
[65] Mumm (1999): 118.

All Saints Convalescent Hospital at Meads, c. 1869, before the Chapel was built

III
The idea of convalescence

In 1837 John Roberton, Surgeon to the Manchester Lying-In Hospital, published what was probably the first article in Britain on the need for convalescent retreats for the poor. Roberton was concerned for the welfare of Manchester's manufacturing communities, about 'the sickliness of the operative poor in a large town.'[66] Wealthy Victorians could travel up the Rhine and convalesce at Wiesbaden and Baden-Baden; what Roberton wanted were the best possible conditions for the poorest convalescents. His outline scheme was based partly on his knowledge of the Hotel Dieu, opened as a convalescent hospital in Paris in 1775: he wanted a retreat built in a salubrious situation, on the coast, optimally six to eight miles from a town, consisting of a 'commodious building' with governor and matron administering say one hundred beds, to be erected by public subscription and sustained by annual subscription, open April until October, with inmates staying for three weeks, given a plain wholesome diet, and attended by a registered apothecary. Roberton estimated that an annual income of £1,200 would allow at least 1,000 adult patients to 'breathe a pure bracing atmosphere, have clean airy lodgings, plenty of wholesome food, and no other duties to perform than those arising from the care of her person, and her daily walks.'[67]

In 1844 Roberton's vision was partially realised, not for Manchester's working poor, but in the foundation of the Metropolitan Convalescent Institution of London, which built a series of large Convalescent Hospitals for the Poor of London, one at Walton, Surrey, two at Bexhill, Sussex, and another at Broadstairs in Kent, each catering either for men, women or children.[68]

It is impossible to know for certain how much Mother Foundress knew about Roberton's vision, about Vincennes Convalescent Hospital in Paris, which opened in 1857, or any other European convalescent hospitals; however, her scheme for the All Saints Convalescent Hospital at Eastbourne was much like Roberton's in its seasonal opening, its system of three-week stays, its admittance by subscription (although All Saints was not built by public subscription but by the individual fundraising efforts and donations of the Sisters of All Saints themselves). It

---

[66] John Roberton, 'Suggestions for establishing Convalescents' Retreats on the Sea Coast, as subservient to the Hospitals and other Medical Charities of large towns' in *Edinburgh Medical and Surgical Journal,* 1st October 1837: 326.
[67] Ibid: 332.
[68] John Bryant, (1927) *Convalescence, Historical and Practical,* The Sturgis Fund of the Burke Foundation, New York: 4.

overlooked the sea, was in reasonable proximity to a town, and provided simple care and wholesome food (much of which was produced in the gardens of the Hospital). Moreover, many of the patients were working women and men 'who were given that change of air that often to them means life instead of death, and gives them the ability to maintain themselves in honest independence.' [69]

Roberton was greatly enamoured by Vincennes Convalescent Hospital, which was set in a forty-acre park and composed of two long wings on either side of a central pavilion; the buildings were laid out from east to west in such a way that the convalescents' living quarters were exposed to the sun at noon. All Saints was also built on an east-west axis, receiving the sun at noon, and perhaps even better than Vincennes, has the advantages of the sea air and the light, described by a writer for *The Philanthropist* in the 1890s as

'the most favourable spot possible for the success of [the Sisters'] benevolent project. To the poor patient, just risen from a sick-bed in a London hospital, a few week's sojourn at this healthy marine resort constitutes an incalculable boon; and the unique position occupied by the All Saints Convalescent Hospital...the only institution of its kind, established particularly for those who require the surgical and medical care and the trained and experienced nursing here provided...*In almost every case, help was given to people unprovided for by other institutions.*'

What we do know is that Mother Foundress was herself a convalescent patient in Eastbourne in 1862 and that her recovery there was so dramatic that she immediately began to make plans for a convalescent home to be run by the All Saints Sisters. Whilst the grand All Saints Convalescent Hospital was being designed and built, she and the Sisters ran a small convalescent home from 1864 to 1867 at Compton Lodge, Eastbourne, listed in the 1867 Post Office Directory as 'All Saints Convalescent Hospital, Hartington Place, President Rt. Hon.

---

[69] *The Philanthropist*, c.1896

Lord Brougham, Hon. Secretary, Sydney Ringer Esq. M.D.'[70] Mother Foundress's recovery was due at least in part to the extremely favourable climatic conditions enjoyed by Eastbourne.[71]

After the Laying of the Foundation Stone of the new All Saints Convalescent Hospital in 1867, the guests were treated to a luncheon of the first delicacies of the season at Compton Lodge, where Reverend Lowe told guests that the big Hospital 'was no new scheme, no untried theory, no visionary idea which had never been put in practice.' He was referring to the fact that the Sisters had been running Compton Lodge as a convalescent hospital for the last three years, and that 'they who had the honour of knowing anything of the work carried on by it could well understand how worthy it was of all classes. About 800 convalescents had already been received, and had all been restored to relative health.' Reverend Lowe added that it would be 'difficult indeed to imagine an undertaking more worthy of the interest and assistance of all good Christian people, for the foundation they were now laying was the foundation of what might indeed be called, in a very real and true sense, the house of God.'[72] No doubt Mother Foundress and the Sisters would have known of the work undertaken by other Sisters caring for soldiers in the Crimea and in the Italian campaigns, where 'Cleanliness, and the encouragement to eat, were recognized as aids to recovery in a situation where no medical antidotes to infection had been discovered.'[73]

Compton Lodge was newly built when the Sisters began to rent it, taking in thirty convalescents at a time. The Sisters probably attended Trinity Church until St. Saviour's was built, and one can imagine them in the South Street area, walking past the brewery and the theatre to collect convalescents from the nearby Station, visiting the site up at Meads that was to become the magnificent All Saints Convalescent Hospital, and fundraising from whatever

---

[70] In the Eastbourne Parish Assessment for 1868 the building is listed as a convalescent hospital but situated in *Trinity* Place, occupied by the 'Sisters of Mercy' and owned by J.L. Parsons, a local stone and marble mason. I am grateful to Vera Hodsell for her assistance regarding this discrepancy.
[71] Described by a local barrister at the time thus '…the proximity of the sea and the peninsular position of the borough ensure equability of climate.' George F. Chambers (1910) *Eastbourne Memories of the Victorian Period 1845-1901*, Sumfield: 180.
[72] *Eastbourne Gazette*, 24th July 1867.
[73] Summers, op.cit: 50.

source possible, since by the time the Foundation Stone was laid, half the funds for the building had yet to be collected, which apparently was not at all unusual in this field of endeavour.[74]

In Britain in 1867 there was no statutory duty to provide convalescent care and even by 1947 the Institute of Almoners had to report that their national study of the 326 convalescent Hospitals (with a total of 138,000 beds) showed that convalescent patients were having to wait six to eight weeks for a bed, facilities were particularly lacking for children, mothers and babies, and teenage boys, and, moreover, that convalescent Hospitals in Great Britain had developed 'without co-ordinated planning and without supervision.'[75] The Report was particularly critical of the fact that many convalescent hospitals imposed hospital standards of discipline, forbidding men and women in the same hospital to meet or go out together, with some hospitals offering no treatment whatsoever. All Saints was one of the culprits here, with strict House Rules and offering no treatment except a 'mild diabetic and gastric diet.' Nevertheless, All Saints Convalescent Hospital stands out as a pioneering, visionary phenomenon, not only at the time of its opening in 1869, but still, by 1895 '…the only institution of its class that admits a patient absolutely free for three weeks on a single subscriber's letter'[76] and able to offer exactly what Dr. Roberton ordered in 1837, for those who would otherwise 'work, and…die before their time…kindness, sleep, quiet, fresh air, and sunshine…'[77]

There was in fact another charitable convalescent home near to Eastbourne, in Seaford, established in 1860: Seaside Convalescent Hospital, with 'invigorating breezes of the sea and the South Downs helped by salt water-baths' which issued tickets for one month a year (over fourteen years the Hospital issued 5,700 tickets) at £1 per patient (although each patient's stay cost the institution £4.15s.). This Hospital operated in distinct contrast to the many private convalescent homes for the wealthy, described by the *Eastbourne Gazette* as those convalescents of 'a selected kind able to command house-lamb in the depth of winter…[and] show as cold a

---

[74] Like Mother Harriet, the Mother Superior at St. John Baptist Convent at Clewer, put her name to the vast amount the enterprise would cost, and then set about raising the funds. The builders and others often had to wait for final payment, according to John Pritchard in correspondence with the author, March 2002.

[75] *Report of the Institute of Almoners on non-profit-making Convalescent Facilities in England and Wales* June 1947: 1.

[76] *The Philanthropist,* c.1896.

[77] A London Physician, in a Letter to the Editor, *The Times,* c.1869.

shoulder as bricks and mortar can to such as cannot patronize early lamb and Scilly Island peas in March.'[78]

So the idea of convalescence was not entirely new at this period, and certainly not to Eastbourne: what was unique to All Saints was that the Foundress Mother 'did not only conceive the plan for Convalescents alone, but also that it *should be worked by Religious* as she had seen and known in Hospitals abroad – also in Building a separate wing for Sisters and ordering a proper Community Room, Refectory and Tribune for the Offices and Hours, where the Novices and young Professed could come and find all Regular and in order for their lives as Religious. The building of the Hospital was a stupendous work and only begun and carried out and completed by the power of prayer and Perseverance… the Clergy and leaders of the Catholic Revival took great interest in the work.'[79]

This, then, was the medical and social context in which All Saints Convalescent Hospital at Eastbourne was built: an urgent need for convalescent hospitals that were free or affordable for working-class people, expanding knowledge about illness and recovery, and the nurse-trained Sisterhoods' desire to 'have the medical staff and work under their own jurisdiction.'[80]

---

[78] *Eastbourne Gazette*, 24th June 1874.
[79] S. Caroline Mary in Mumm (2001): 13.
[80] Mumm (1999): 117.

Laying the Foundation Stone of All Saints Hospital, 1867

IV
'The modern history of Meads may be said to commence with the opening of the All Saints Convalescent Hospital'[81]

When the foundation stone of All Saints Convalescent Hospital was laid on 19th July 1867, the site consisted of cornfields, the Downs were yellow and red with mustard and poppies, oxen could have been ploughing the fields. The Hospital stands at the southern extremity of Meads, adjoining Holywell, about a mile and half from what was then the rapidly expanding town of Eastbourne, protected by the South Downs 'which stretch north by north-west in almost endless configurations…bounded on the south-east and east by the noble cliffs, for the majestic grandeur of which the place is renowned.'[82] The Hospital was sheltered from piercing winds by the rising ground in front of the building, and the chosen site was 'so naturally adapted that the air coming in this direction must be amply rarified, and…being within a few minutes' walk of the edge of the cliffs themselves, a better spot for convalescents, or invalids of any kind, could scarcely be conceived.'[83]

Until that time, Meads, originally developed round a Manor House (later named Coltstocks), was scarcely known; the 1855 Post Office Directory describes the area as a poor agricultural hamlet, half a mile to the south of the town, amongst the South Downs 'where the ortolan or wheatear can be caught,' and lists the occupations and talents of some of the local people thus: John Coleman, lime burner; Coppard & Newman, shopkeepers: Dennis Coppard, beer retailer and shoemaker; John Filder, farmer; Arthur Gearing of 'The Ship' and a butcher; Joseph Gorringe, farmer; James Newman, blacksmith; Samuel Read, wheelwright, Reverend George Stokes, Curate of St. Mary's Church; and a Major George Spiller. 'Gentry' lists only Robert Marriott Caldicott, Esq. at Meads Lodge, the 'Caldecott' who created what was later to become Mother Foundress's religious garden (on land now belonging to St. Andrew's School). The flint-built Holywell Priory[84] stood where Holywell Close is today, thought once to be a smugglers'

---

[81] Chambers, op.cit: 180.
[82] *Eastbourne Gazette*, 24th July 1867.
[83] Ibid.
[84] Demolished in 1897.

inn. Holywell used to be a chalk pit with 'tiny streams of fresh water bursting through the chalk cliffs…Nearby…a little chapel of St. Gregory. The Chapel has long ago disappeared, but health-giving properties were doubtless once associated with these springs, and won for them the name of Holywell…'[85]

In his childhood memoirs, Nelson Gausden (born in Meads in 1893) refers to a Fire Station opposite the Ship, run by local volunteers (and perhaps built on account of the Hospital), a small infants school, and a deserted farmhouse on the corner of Matlock Road.[86] The land on which St. Andrew's School now stands was part of Coltstocks Farm. In a photograph taken around 1881 from the Downs above Duke's Drive, one can see Holywell Priory in the foreground, owned then by Countess de Noailles, an eccentric woman who allegedly kept a cow under her bedroom and had a shaft built to let the air rise, which she considered beneficial to health. In the photograph there are posts and lines across the lane, clothes lines belonging to families in the area: 'Washing was mangled in a small stone hut known as "The Mangle Room" in this lane.'[87] Behind Gausden's own house, one of the flint Hart's Cottages beside the Pilot Inn, was a blacksmith's forge, and across the land a large barn facing Beachy Head.

According to an Indenture dated 22nd March 1867 between 'the Most Noble William Duke of Devonshire and Miss Harriet Brownlow Byron,' the area on which the Hospital was to stand was 'all that piece or parcel of land situate at Meads…containing 4 acres 3 roods and 12 perches' sold to Mother Foundress by the Duke of Devonshire for £1,730.'[88] The Duke stipulated that Mother Foundress would require written consent from himself or his heirs to' build or erect any building or edifice…other than a Hospital with the necessary offices and outbuildings…and a Chapel.' The Mother Superior would be responsible for any expenses incurred by the Duke in paving and curbing the footpaths, and the channelling and flinting of the roadways on the north and south sides.[89] Mother Foundress was also bound to pay to the Duke a fair proportion of the expense of constructing and maintaining any main sewer, plus at her own expense make all necessary drains and connections for draining the premises into such

---

[85] From 'A Little Guide to All Saints Hospital, Eastbourne,' c.1930s (unpaginated).

[86] Nelson Gausden,, 'My Childhood Days in Meads Village,' *Eastbourne Local History Newsletter*, No.15, April 1975: 4-5.

[87] From handwritten notes attached to this photograph, Eastbourne Reference Library.

[88] Cited in the *Abstract of the Title Deeds,* 19th July 1869.

[89] The roads around the site were not yet made – Darley Road was made in 1890, and Duke's Drive, later King Edward's Parade, in 1892.

main sewer. The Duke gave her permission to erect an entrance lodge,[90] and asked that he see any plans for enlargements or additions.

The *Abstracts of the Title* dated 17th and 19th July 1869 show that Mother Foundress paid a further £2,721.5.0 for another piece of land, '1 acre, one rood and 28 perches abutting South upon the Cliff Road West.' Then to pay for the completion of the Hospital and other buildings (although not the Chapel), Mother Foundress borrowed £10,000 from the Duke, repayable with interest at a rate of £5.1.0% p.a., to be paid off by January 1870. Mother Foundress was to have control of receipts and expenditure on the Hospital and power to draw money from the Bankers, but it was expressly declared that the loan was to be paid off before any expenditure was made or debt incurred in the building of the Chapel. Meanwhile the Trustees of the Hospital were to be liable for monies received 'by virtue of the trusts in them reposed…and should be answerable for any losses.' The Trustees at this time were Sir Edward Hulse, Baronet, Sir William Jenner, Baronet, The Reverend William Upton Richards, and George Augustus Jeffery, M.D.

According to an Eastbourne barrister of the time, George Chambers 'The fact that the great Convalescent Hospital had been put there, perhaps suggested to some people that Meads had a future, whilst others believed that the site of the Hospital was chosen because the locality was so entirely out of the way, that it never would have a future so far as the growth of East-Bourne as a fashionable watering-place was concerned.'[91]

Perhaps the local cynics were shortly able to revise their view: the founders and Trustees of the Hospital and indeed the physicians who were to give their services to the Hospital entirely free, were in fact as wealthy and fashionable as anyone. From the beginning the All Saints Sisters had gathered a great coterie of wealthy philanthropic friends, supporters and patrons - including Prince Christian of Schleswig-Holstein, the Prince and Princess of Wales, and none other than Queen Victoria herself, who made a donation and 'became an annual subscriber of ten guineas for the benefit of any member of the Royal Household who might require a letter of

---

[90] Now South Lodge, sold into private hands in 2001.
[91] Chambers, op.cit: 180.

Patronage: The Prince and Princess of Wales with guests of the Duke of Devonshire, Compton Place, Eastbourne, 1883

admission'[92] - and some of whom were there in the procession at the Laying of the Foundation Stone of All Saints Convalescent Hospital.

On that day, 19th July 1867, a large stone cube was suspended ready under an awning. At one o'clock a procession formed in an outbuilding, led by the Reverend T. Lowe, Rural Dean and Vicar of Willingdon, representing the Bishop of Chichester who wished the Sisters' enterprise well but thought he should not be seen to be supporting the idea of Church of England religious communities. Henry Woodyer was also in the procession, and Dr. Jeffery, the physician to the Hospital, along with a 'large company of ladies and gentlemen' and a number of Sisters. The architect presented Lady Fanny Howard (the Duke of Devonshire's sister, living with her brother at Compton Place at this time) with a silver and ivory trowel and she 'manipulated the prepared cement with graceful skill,' completing this part of the ceremony by etching the stone three times with a mallet in the name of the Father, the Son and the Holy Ghost, after which the All Saints Margaret Street choir, in their white surplices, sang 'Christ is made the sure foundation'[93] and Mr. C.W. Ewing, organist of St. Saviour's Church, presided at the harmonium.

Exactly two years later, on 19th July 1869, All Saints Convalescent Hospital was declared open by Bishop Samuel Wilberforce, by then Bishop of Winchester 'and a large concourse of *leading* Cathedral clergy and laymen and Outer Sisters and friends from London and all parts… [and] no trees or garden or wall around – so much exposed to the public and…after the function was over and we sisters had collected round our Mother Foundress in the Community Room, we had to pull down *blinds* as the people from the town came and looked through the windows *at the Sisters* who were then '*wonder!*' and a *sight* quite out of the way in those days.'[94]

The Hospital was described by a reporter in the *British Medical Journal* as 'magnificent in size and architecture, and displays in all respects excellent taste. It is by far the largest and most ornamental erection in Eastbourne.' However, the *Journal* did not 'intend to imply an

---

[92] Denys Giddey (undated) *The Story of All Saints Hospital, Eastbourne:* 16. The first of several editions of Canon Giddey's history of All Saints was published c.1967. Canon Giddey was Chaplain to the Eastbourne Group of Hospitals, of which All Saints was one of seven, from 1961-83).

[93] Sister Hildegard's handwritten notes: 1, All Saints Archive. S. Hildegard was Headmistress of the All Saints Sisters' St. Cyprians School for Girls in the Cape, South Africa 1902-1924.

[94] S. Caroline Mary, in Mumm (2001): 18.Original emphasis.

unqualified approval of the palatial style of building, which is, indeed, in some respects inappropriate to a Hospital for invalids. The lofty staircases…emulate those of the largest hotels, and must be a serious inconvenience to those who ought to have every facility of access to the fresh air. A series of small buildings, none more than two stories high, would suit our notions better. A convalescent village…It must take many persons a month to feel settled in such a magnificent building…'[95]

What the magnificent building actually consisted of was in fact '…in plan mainly parallelogram 340 ft in length, divided by party wall into men's and women's sides or wings, which are for the most part alike and consist each of a central pavilion containing stone staircases etc which give access to all the wards. On the ground floor, two convalescent day wards, two smaller rooms for patients requiring separate treatment and large ward for incurable cases. Every large ward has attached to it a nurses' and sisters' room overlooking it, and lavatories, baths and other ample conveniences in small projecting wings, ensuring thereby thorough ventilation. The South wing is the sisters' house. When the building is completed, funds are still wanted for chapel and dining-hall. Attention has been paid to ventilation, drainage and warming (with hot water). Red brick with Bath stone doors and windows of Geometrical Gothic, plain tiled, blue or grey Forest of Dean stone being used for main piers and steps of staircase, window shafts, etc. Cost of building now constructed and enclosing walls, gardener's lodge and chaplain's apartments estimated at £36,000; of this £26,000 is already subscribed.'[96]

Mother Foundress's Hospital has two and a half storeys with a 'variety of ashlar-framed windows with elaborate tracery distinctive of Woodyer's style. The high-pitched roof has attics lit by dormer windows. The tall chimneys which originally rose above the roof line have since been reduced in height. The gabled east and west ends of the main building, and the south end of the south wing, all have a balcony on the first floor formed by an arcade of pointed arches, with a similar arcade on the ground floor. An entrance porch, with arched doorway and a pyramidal roof containing dormers on three sides, is set cater-cornered in the junction of the main building and the south wing.'[97]

---

[95] 'The Convalescent Hospital at Eastbourne,' by our own Reporter, *British Medical Journal*, 7th May, 1870: 460.
[96] *The Builder*, Vol.XXVII (1869): 613.
[97] John Elliott & John Pritchard, eds (2002) *Henry Woodyer, Gentleman Architect*, University of Reading: 240.

It is thought that the Hospital was built to accommodate up to 300 patients but the number cited by different sources ranges between 100 and 900. In reality, the Hospital was probably able to receive about 100 patients initially, that number rising to over 200 when the new wing was built in 1887. The Chapel was built in 1874 to accommodate 300, to include patients, Sisters, clergy and visitors. The Hospital, when completed, contained separate wards for men, women, and children, several day rooms for the different stages of convalescence, and separate refectories or dining-halls for the male and female patients. As the *Eastbourne Gazette* commented:

'In truth there is such accommodation offered for convalescents that more than one visitor of good means expressed their opinion that even in the homes of the wealthy such an amount of care was not provided for those of the family who may be in weak health. It is not only that the exterior of the building is very pleasing to the eye - and the ground when laid out, will undoubtedly make it more so – but the interior is so economized in space and the general arrangements so perfect, that many could not help expressing the wish also that were ill health to attend them they should prefer the comforts which the Eastbourne Convalescent Hospital seems likely to afford…It is a noble structure…noble is the object aimed at by the promoters, and noble is the work to which free and willing hands – we mean the Sisters and their attendants – have subjected themselves.'[98]

No doubt the interior accommodation was designed with concern for ventilation, light and warmth in the context of knowledge of other Hospitals being built at this time. However, All Saints Convalescent Hospital is highly idiosyncratic. For example, its two main entrances, one for men and one for women, hidden from each other by the south wing (the Sisters' administrative and living accommodation), are similar but not identical. Moreover, the entrances jut suddenly at right angles from a corner, they consist of a middle-pointed doorway, oak door, tiled roof with three dormer windows, a statue of Christ healing the sick at the men's entrance, and the Madonna and Child at the women's entrance, and in the roof of each porch is a symbolic chapter room (*parvis*). Another example: on each floor, the windows are placed at

---

[98] *Eastbourne Gazette*, 21st July 1869.

different heights, some with long sloping sills, others with short sloping sills; the lintel stones and facings round the windows are sometimes asymmetrical.

Some of these design features are to do with locality and materials; other features can be attributed to Henry Woodyer's interest in Gothic Revivalist principles; yet others to the architect's whimsical approach. For example, there are many different patterns in the plate tracery[99] of the Hospital windows and arches (and again in the Chapel). One goes round the back of the Hospital into the courtyard (to the mortuary, stables, laundry and kitchens) and encounters a startling Normandy-style turreted tower up to roof level, topped with a small flag.[100] The tower provides, in fact, what appears to be a fire escape from additional wards built

[99] Plate tracery was the simplest form of Gothic tracery where the lights appear cut through solid stone. Its muscularity made it a particular favourite of High Victorian architects.
[100] Woodyer built similar turrets at his own country house and at St. John Baptist Convent, Clewer.

in 1880, although the spiral staircase is made of wood. The upper windows of the Hospital pierce the roofline of the building, and a variety of nun-like dormer windows grace the roofs. Narrow turrets cling to the first and second floors – they are surveillance towers for the wards, and even they don't have identical buttresses. The drain heads vary in size, and there is tapered brickwork on the base of the chimneys, repeated in some of the corners.

Then at each end of the Hospital and at the back of the Sisters' wing there are balconies formed by arcades of pointed arches, perhaps twelve feet high. As you look out from the wards, those middle-pointed arches draw your eye upwards and frame the sky: for a moment you sense the grandeur – not of the arches – but of the sky, of God's beautiful sky. Below, in the stone balustrade, is more tracery, this time four leaved clovers. In fact, the following could easily refer to the All Saints Sisters and their Hospital – in the words of Dinah Mulock Craik:

'Every religious community…should combine, if possible, Beauty with Duty…I was glad to see that this particular Sisterhood had made their own dress, and that of their orphans, as picturesque as possible; that their building within and without was not only convenient but elegant, and their chapel and its service as beautiful as God's house should be. And why not? Lives devoted to duty cannot afford to have any beauty taken out of them.'[101]

So who was Henry Woodyer? How could he have brought this building to Meads, a building so full of contradictions: beautiful and ugly, optimistic yet punitive, all Gothic yet *witty* - and full of mystery?

---

[101] Craik, op.cit: 57.

V
Henry Woodyer
Gentleman Architect

'Tall, rather spare; always attired in an easy-fitting blue serge suit, loose shirt collar and crimson silk tie… soft black hat – rather wide at the brim …long dark Inverness cloak… A most picturesque figure, often smoking an extremely fragrant cigar.'[102]

'his buildings were for the glory of God, not his own fame'[103]

Henry Woodyer was born in Guildford, Surrey in 1816 and died at Padworth Common, Berkshire in 1896. His father, Caleb Woodyer was a surgeon and a male accoucheur (a birth assistant); his mother, Mary Anne Halsey, was one of the babies that his father delivered. In 1829 Henry went to Eton, becoming the first Old Etonian to practise architecture. Here he came under the influence of Edward Coleridge (the poet Coleridge's nephew) who was to become an active follower of the Oxford Movement, and in 1835, at the height of the religious fervour generated by that Movement, Henry became a student at Merton College, Oxford. In 1839 he was apparently attending lectures by the Oxford Regius Professor of Divinity, and at that time remained uncertain of his professional direction. His Eton friend, Thomas Gambier Parry, said that when Woodyer left Oxford, architecture was 'the last profession he thought of, he never dreamt he was fit for it…'[104]

However, by 1842 Woodyer was designing church fittings in Guildford, and around this time may have been in contact with Pugin's architectural office in London. Augustus Welby Northmore Pugin (1812-1852) was the most revolutionary and influential of the Gothic architects – amongst many famous works he is known for designing the Palace of Westminster and St. George's Catholic Cathedral in Southwark. He also wrote the voluminous *Glossary of*

---

[102] Harry Redfern, 'Some Recollections of William Butterfield and Henry Woodyer,' a paper read before the Ecclesiological Society, printed in *The Architect and Building News*, 14th April 1944: 22.
[103] John Elliott & John Pritchard, eds (2002) *Henry Woodyer, Gentleman Architect*, University of Reading: 9.
[104] Ibid: 13.

Eccesiastical Ornament and Costume (1858) which involved years of laborious research into English and European religious practice and symbolism in the medieval period. His work formed the basis of the principles adopted by the Ecclesiological Society: that form should follow function, and that the type of buildings a society produces is a reflection of the spiritual condition of that society – and, moreover, can assist in reforming that spiritual state.[105] John Ruskin didn't always appreciate Pugin's efforts, however, on one occasion accusing Pugin of blaming the ugliness of his designs in Southwark Cathedral on lack of funds: '…was it want of money that made you put that blunt, overloaded, laborious ogee door into the side…that you sunk the tracery of the parapet in its clumsy zigzags…that you buried its paltry pinnacles in that eruption of diseased crockets?'[106]

Thus we have Florence Nightingale's hostility towards the nursing Sisterhoods, and John Ruskin's hostility towards the master of Gothic. However, Nightingale also needed the Sisters, and Ruskin was in fact a supporter of the Gothic Revival, advocating the use of chequers, zig-zags, stripes and geometrical colour mosaic in his *The Seven Lamps of Architecture.*[107]

By 1845 Woodyer had his own office at 108 High Street, Guildford, the same address as his father's medical practice, and was receiving a steady stream of commissions, mostly from contacts made at Eton and Oxford and by personal recommendation from other High Anglican churchmen. Henry Woodyer was emerging now as an independently minded gentleman architect who 'began with his feet planted on ground that Pugin had leveled in the 1830s and 1840s.'[108] Between 1845 and 1847 he built his first church, for his brother-in-law, at Wyke, near Guildford.

In 1849 Henry Woodyer's father died, leaving his son several properties in Stoke and Guildford: Woodyer was now financially independent and free to offer his services without charge to causes he believed in. Between 1849 and 1851 he built the famous Highnam Church in Gloucestershire as a memorial for Gambier Parry's wife. Here he worked with Pugin's builder, George Myers, and developed working relationships with some of the best craftsmen and workmen of the period: Hardman, Clayton & Bell, Kempe, and Wailes of Newcastle for

---

[105] Julian Orbach (1987), *Blue Guide to Victorian Architecture in Britain*, A & C Black: 11.

[106] Cited in Benjamin Ferrey (1978) *Recollections of A.W.N. Pugin and his father Augustus Pugin*, The Scholar Press: 165.

[107] John Ruskin (1849) *The Seven Lamps of Architecture,*1904 edition published by George Allen.

[108] Anthony Quiney, in an article on Woodyer in *Architectural History*, Vol.38 (1995), cited by Tom Fenton (2002) *To Raise a Perfect Monument to Taste* (private publication): 7.

The 'women's' entrance to All Saints Convalescent Hospital

glass, Hardman also for brass and ironwork, and Herbert Minton for floor tiles. The consecration of Highnam Church in April 1851 coincided with the Great Exhibition, for which Hardman kept back two of the chandeliers meant for Parry's church.

In 1851 Woodyer married Martha Bowles and on 2nd June 1852 his daughter was born, Hester Fanny. His wife Martha tragically died later that month, on 21st June: Hester Fanny became Woodyer's constant companion (he never married again), only leaving her father when she was thirty-nine to marry and live in Canada. In 1854 Woodyer built his own house at Grafham in Surrey, and set up his office at home: according to William Redfern, who was a Clerk at this office, he attended to his own correspondence in an undecipherable hand, he wasn't a brilliant draughtsman but able to illustrate his own designs clearly - and not just for buildings, he also designed church furniture, ironwork (see his famous 'Burning Bush' lamp outside Eton College), patterns for tiles and walls, busts and doors, and worked very closely with his stained glass window designers, Hardman Powell - and he ran a small staff of elderly and well-tried assistants brought up in his own ways.[109] Woodyer frequently sailed in the Mediterranean on his 59ft yacht which he called the *Queen Mab,* further evidence of the man's wit: *Queen Mab* is the title of a poem by the fiercely atheist Percy Bysshe Shelley. 1858-9 saw him restoring Eton College Hall, and in 1860-1861 building a church at Grafham as a memorial to his own wife; by 1861 his estate occupied 300 acres.

From 1846 to 1857 Woodyer was listed in London Post Office directories as an architect at 4 Adam Street, Adelphi, William Butterfield's office. Apart from his famous All Saints, Margaret Street, Butterfield is known for his work on the Beresford-Hope mediaeval buildings of St. Augustine at Canterbury, turning them into a missionary college, and employing a 'somewhat strange version of Gothic.'[110] Butterfield was elected to the Ecclesiological Society in 1844, and was made an Honorary Member of the Oxford Architectural Society in 1848. Both these societies contributed to *Instrumenta Ecclesiastica*, two books of model designs published by the Ecclesiological Society. Woodyer apparently believed in the value of these collected designs – in fact he produced some of the designs for the second edition of *Instrumenta* Ecclesiastica - and derived ideas for his works from them, although according to Redfern, who also worked in

---

[109] Redfern, op.cit: 22.
[110] Ibid: 21

Butterfield's office, Woodyer's outlook on architecture was entirely different from that of Butterfield:

'as was only to be expected since their temperaments were as the poles apart. But they had in common an intense dislike to anything that savoured of professionalism or of publicity: and would not permit their designs to be published…amongst contemporary architects, only Street was a more or less distant friend…'[111]

The influences of Pugin and Butterfield are evident in some of Woodyer's work but other styles and precedents across Europe played an important part in his designs, and although retaining 'steady fidelity to the Middle-pointed' style, he didn't usually copy Decorated prototypes directly. His work is identifiable by its 'spiky window tracery, sharp, polygonal cusping on doorways and porches, flamboyant bargeboards and distinctive gabled dormers'[112] and he has been praised for being able 'to catch the spirit of Old English work without imitating it.'[113]

By the time he was creating All Saints Convalescent Hospital with its characteristic 'contorted, nervy lines' and 'terse, agitated quality,'[114] Woodyer had employed his particular talents not only in Highnam Church and Eton College, but also designing a House of Mercy (the Convent of St. John Baptist) at Clewer, near Windsor and also at Clewer, in 1865-6, St. Andrew's Convalescent Hospital (with 64 beds) and in a range of other projects:

'today, I have visited a house some 9 miles from this and a Church 4 miles farther – on Monday I must visit a large middle School and a College I am building. On Tuesday a man is coming here to consult me about his Church in Sussex. On Wed. I must go to Eastbourn [sic] where I

---

[111] Ibid. George Street designed St. Saviour's Church, South Street, Eastbourne, the church attended by the Sisters of All Saints between 1869 and 1873, before their new Chapel was built.

[112] Ibid.

[113] Charles Eastlake (1872) *A History of the Gothic Revival*, ed. Mordaunt Crook (1978): 328, cited in Ellis & Pritchard, op.cit: 15.

[114] Anthony Quiney, "Altogether a capital fellow and a serious fellow too": a brief account of the life and work of Henry Woodyer 1816-1896,' *Architectural History*, 38 (1995): 192-219, cited in Elliott & Pritchard, op.cit: 31.

The Memorial Tablet to Henry Wooder, on the south wall of the Chapel at Clewer Convent. The central figure is a representation of Woodyer.

52

am building a Hospital for some 300 inmates, on Thursday business in London, Friday to Beaconsfield, a Church & House. Saturday to [?] a large new Church…'[115]

Woodyer's work at Clewer gives us some insight into his religious concerns, and helps to explain his connection with the All Saints Sisters of the Poor. The House of Mercy was established in 1849 by Mariquita Tennant as a women's refuge in response to local need for the care of 'fallen women' or 'penitents'. The definition of 'penitent' was not restricted to repentant prostitutes: the term applied to any woman 'who had deviated from conventional sexual morality,' for example, a woman cohabiting with a man, or a victim of incest. By 1903 there were no less than 238 Anglican penitentiaries, 200 of which were directed by Sisterhoods.[116] The mostly working-class penitents lived closely with their middle-class sisters who trained them for higher levels of domestic service (particularly laundry and needlework) in a radical arrangement, the justification for which 'stemmed from the scriptural encounter between Jesus and Mary Magdalene. While society passed sentence of "utter, final ex-communication" on the fallen, the Church did not.'[117]   In 1852 the House was taken over by the Community of St. John Baptist, founded by Harriet Monsell, who was Mother Superior until 1875 (she attended the opening of All Saints Hospital).

Woodyer's support for this mission (known to him through his friend Canon Thomas Thellusson Carter, Rector of the nearby St. Andrew's Church) led to his overseeing of 'building work for the next thirty years without ever charging a fee for his designs or supervision.'[118] In 1853 Woodyer drew up plans for a complex of buildings and by 1857 had accommodation for thirty-eight penitents and eleven sisters; by mid-1858 work was completed on the south range and a chapel; the red-brick cloistered building had a water tower which supplied the laundry and an infirmary with an oriel window into the adjacent chapel so the sick could hear the services. By 1875 there were up to eighty penitents and 138 sisters, and Woodyer had designed for the Clewer Sisterhood an orphanage, a convalescent hospital, a school, two houses and a new, elaborate chapel, of which the chapel at All Saints may be said to be a prototype: the Clewer

---

[115] Upton St. Leonards correspondence, 3rd March 1852, fol.56 (Gordon Barnes Papers, Council for the Care of Churches library) cited in Elliott & Pritchard, op.cit: 23.

[116] Mumm (1999): 99.

[117] Ibid: 100. This was in contrast to secular institutions which encouraged penitents to emigrate.

[118] Elliott & Pritchard, op.cit: 99.

chapel is very similar (in particular, the single roof over the nave and chancel, the polygonal apse with painted ceiling, the polychromatic interior brickwork) but much more elaborate. Woodyer's buildings at Clewer are regarded by some as the pinnacle of his architectural, and perhaps his religious, achievement, and provide a distinct paradigm within which we can consider his design of All Saints Convalescent Hospital and Chapel.

Woodyer was a gracious and thoughtful man: responding to Parry's enquiry about placing a bust of his wife in the new church at Highnam, Woodyer writes '…there is no authority for a bust that I am sure of in English architecture. However, feelings for those that are taken are sacred and may not be judged by cold rules of right or wrong.'[119] He was humane: at Clewer he refused to alter plans for a passage which would have condemned half of the Sisters' rooms to face north instead of south.'[120] Henry Woodyer had the sensibility of an artist as much as an architect, apparent in this letter to Gambier Parry:

'My ideal of a spire is I think very close to yours; the best grouping of pinnacles that has presented itself to my eyes is that of St. Mary's at Oxford. The spire itself is not lofty enough for you but the outline of its pinnacles as seen through a mist or haze is just the hint one wants.'[121]

This sensibility may also explain his dislike of professionalism and his refusal to actively promote his work. His decision to work mainly as a church architect was driven by a sense of religious vocation, by love: 'his buildings were for the glory of God, not his own fame.'[122] Of himself he said 'I am inclined to be a Reformer of conventional forms & drawing…be kind enough to remember that my love is all taken from detailed inspection of and living amongst these old forms of beauty, an Ecclesiastical Architect who feels his work lives as it were in a new-old world.'[123]

---

[119] Fenton, op.cit: 9.
[120] Elliott & Pritchard, op.cit: 26.
[121] Ibid: 16.
[122] Elliott & Pritchard, op.cit: 13.
[123] Cited in Fenton, op.cit: 8-9.

Ten years before the opening of Woodyer's All Saints Hospital, Henry Currey (1820-1900) had been appointed 'Architect to (His Grace) the Duke of Devonshire'[124] in Eastbourne, and had designed the whole area south of Compton Place down to the sea, bordered by Sea Houses to the east and Meads to the West – Hartington Place, Burlington Place, Chiswick Place and Devonshire Place, Eastbourne College, the walks and terraces along the seafront, the Winter Garden with its glass Pavilion and Floral Hall, Queen's Hotel, Bedford Well Pumping Station, Devonshire Park Theatre, and St. Peter's Church. Like Woodyer, Currey went to Eton (1833-37) and then took articles with the architect Decimus Burton who was working on the Great Conservatory at Chatsworth, the largest glass building in the world. It was Burton whom the Duke of Devonshire (then Lord Burlington) commissioned to prepare the first development plan for the town soon after he inherited Compton Place and the Eastbourne Estate in 1834. Burton designed Eastbourne's Trinity Chapel in the Gothic style in 1838 and produced a plan for Meads, but after this there were no major developments until 1847 when a local surveyor was appointed to 'set out and survey a portion of Eastbourne.'[125] The opening of the Branch Railway from Polegate to Eastbourne in 1849, now bringing visitors all the way from London, gave Lord Burlington the impetus to proceed, and the foundation of the new town was laid in 1851, beginning with several terraces (Victoria Place, the west side of Cavendish Place and the block which includes Burlington Hotel). It was after Lord Burlington became the Seventh Duke of Devonshire in 1858 that he began to consider the second phase, thus appointing Currey in 1859.

In 1847 Currey had become greatly enamoured with Italy, especially Venice. His Italianate style is embodied in the formal parts of Eastbourne, in Devonshire Place (1874), the Devonshire Park Theatre (1884), and in his most significant national achievement, St. Thomas's Hospital in Southwark, London (opened in 1868 by Queen Victoria), where originally each ward had its own balcony on which patients could sit and look the River Thames, the whole design facilitating the circulation of air. In a similar, though secular, partnership to that of Mother Foundress and Henry Woodyer, Henry Currey worked closely with Florence Nightingale, who influenced that Hospital's design considerably, for example 'as in the rounded corners of the wards, so designed that no dust would accumulate there.'[126]

---

[124] Richard N. Crook (1978) 'Henry Currey and the Seventh Duke of Devonshire,' unpublished thesis: 59.
[125] Ibid:56.
[126] Ibid: 28.

However, Currey also produced buildings that had a more vernacular style, with semi-Gothic features: Eastbourne College (1871), for example, and its Chapel, which opened the same year as the Chapel at All Saints Hospital (1874). This style is found again in houses along a grid of tree-lined avenues leading west out of the main town towards Meads and All Saints – in Furness Road, Buxton Road and Carlisle Road, for example – 'red brick and steeply pitched roofs with a multitude of gables and dormers projecting here there and everywhere.'[127] This grid was Currey's second Design, a westerly continuation of his 1859 plan. It is possible that the way in which All Saints' Gothic style dominates this area encouraged Currey to use the same style in the roads that lead up to the Hospital. Currey's last work for Eastbourne, St. Peter's Church (1894) was built of stone, without a tower, but 'impressive by the long row of Early English Arcading…'[128] Currey continued to work until he died in 1900, having been, unlike Woodyer, only too happy to be a professional architect, elected to FRIBA in 1856 and its Vice President 1874-1877 and 1889-1893.

Blessed with the charms of the local architecture and wide even roads, the population of Eastbourne (5,795 in 1862) was also beginning to experience the delights of having a main sewer, opened by the Duke in May 1867 at Langney Point, and in the same year the promise of new sites for reservoirs and gas works. In 1867 St. Saviour's Church was under construction in South Street, on land given by the Duke of Devonshire; local people could drink water that was 'free from colour, and…containing a remarkably small proportion of organic matter';[129] and the town was lit by gas (Eastbourne Electric Light Company was formed in 1881). A road from the Grand Parade to Holywell was being built, the first pile of the pier had been laid, letters were despatched for London and all parts twice a day. The Duke of Devonshire and Mrs. Davies Gilbert were the principal landowners, there were nine places of worship, including a new Wesleyan Chapel, a Calvinist Independent Chapel and the early Gothic St. Mary's Church, a workhouse for two hundred inmates, two national schools, three infant schools, four hotels and a number of lodging houses, and *thirty-one* insurance agents. Of course 1867 is also the year the Duke of Devonshire sold Mother Foundress five acres of land at Meads for her grand Hospital.

---

[127] Crook, op.cit: 72.
[128] Pevsner, cited by Crook, op.cit: 108.
[129] *Sussex Post Office Directory* (1867)

VI
Mortal labour:
building All Saints Convalescent Hospital

All Saints Convalescent Hospital, south wing

The great processions of Sisters in the nineteenth century were matched by great processions of highly skilled engineers, artisans, builders and labourers. This part of the book is an investigation of the almost insurmountable task of turning Mother Foundress's dream into material form.

Woodyer's builders were Wheeler Bros. of Reading, chosen no doubt for their competitive tender but also because of their high quality work. Between 1853 and 1892 Samuel Wheeler (mason and works manager) and Samuel Wheeler Junior (pupil at Reading School of Art and founder in 1885 of Tilehurst Potteries) worked on thirty-nine building projects for Woodyer and attended his funeral in 1896. Woodyer also employed stonemasons and stone carvers, consistently T. Nicholls of Lambeth; George Minton, tile manufacturers; Rattee & Kett of Cambridge, woodcarvers; foundry-workers and iron-workers, usually Filmer & Mason of Guildford, for example for the characteristic dated rainwater heads, and occasionally a local blacksmith; engineers, polishers, marble workers, plumbers, carpenters, brick-makers and labourers.

Whilst Henry Currey designed grand, classical Italianate buildings using stone dressings (stucco or render) over brick, Woodyer preferred to explore the effects of exposed brick. Both architects would have had several reasons for choosing brick: first of all it was much cheaper than quarrying, shaping and transporting large quantities of stone, especially since the ending of the Brick Tax in 1850.[130] Brick-makers and bricklayers were cheaper to employ than the more militant skilled stonemasons. A moulded brick is determined by the size of a man's hand, therefore bricks have uniformity, making their mass production – especially now that the old hand-process had been mechanized (late 1850s, early 1860s) – highly economical. Brick doesn't deteriorate like stone, it is non-combustible (unlike wood or lathe and plaster); being porous it is not a good conductor and is therefore warm in winter and cool in summer (the opposite of glass). Bricks could be supplied from local pits, possibly from the clay pit of Rodwell & Ashton at Crowborough, which by 1887 was sending in by rail to Eastbourne four million bricks a year.[131]

What is important for our visual perception is that the brick as a unit militates against grandeur. It is anti-monumental, an aggregation of small effects. It implies a human and

---

[130] According to the Guide to *All Saints Margaret Street,* op.cit: 6, in 1847 (before the ending of the Brick Tax) William Butterfield apparently paid more for the pink brick he chose for All Saints, Margaret Street, than he would have paid for stone.

[131] M.J. Cruttenden, 'Eastbourne's Industrial Sidings' in *Eastbourne Local History Newsletter*, No.62, 1986: 15*n.*

intimate quality not present to the same extent in stone architecture.[132] This seems particularly fitting for Woodyer and Mother Foundress's vision: for Mother Foundress, humility was the important, and perhaps the hardest, thing; and for Woodyer, dedication to the principles of Gothic architecture[133] together with a natural, devotional humility.

Bath stone was used to create the carved, Geometric Gothic door and window surrounds of the Hospital. ('Bath stone' is used generically to denote the product of many Great Oolite quarries. In the 1850s and 60s George Myers, Pugin's chief builder, leased underground Bath stone quarries in Wiltshire). The building of the Kennet and Avon Canal facilitated the transport of stone from Box in Gloucestershire and other nearby quarries, and with the completion of the Box tunnel and coming of the Great Western Railway in 1841, overland transport became much cheaper, and the price of Bath stone was therefore much reduced.[134] Myers would probably have used stone from these quarries to build for example Pugin's Cathedral in Southwark, for which Pugin had specified 'the whole of the dressings, external and internal, moulds, string courses, water tables, jambs, arches, tracery, copings, pillars, arches, etc., to be worked in the best Bath stone.'[135] Pugin believed the stone to be the best that could be employed, 'that it was far superior to Caen stone and that when it was taken from the right quarry, it was of a very durable description.' Blue or grey Forest of Dean Stone is one of the strongest, although one of the least attractive, and too hard for ornamentation: this was the stone used for the main piers and steps of the Hospital's grand 'flying staircase.'

The soft wood used by the building trade at this time frequently came from the Baltic, fir trees being imported in large quantities from Danzig and Riga. Hardwoods were widely available, but in the Hospital oak was selected for all the doors, the banisters, the 'helical' staircases in the turret rooms overlooking the main wards, and in the Chapel and the Tribune.

---

[132] Alec Clifton-Taylor (1972) *The Pattern of English Building*, Faber & Faber: 242.

[133] In fact, William Butterfield, amongst the Ecclesiologists, made it his personal mission to "give dignity to brick" and his All Saints, Margaret Street, became the model on which Gothic Revivalist architects subsequently designed their churches. See Guide to *All Saints, Margaret Street* op.cit: 6.

[134] In fact, the use of polychromy (varied colours in architecture and decoration) in the new Gothic buildings, was made possible partly by the new railway system which by 1852 reached Aberdeen and Cornwall, and by 1874, the tip of Scotland. Aberdeen granite, Midland red sandstone, Welsh and Cornish slate, Bath and Portland stone, as well as the products of manufacture, terracotta and cast iron, could be sent by rail throughout the country.

[135] The foundation stone of the Cathedral had to be laid very early in the morning, in secret, for fear of anti-Popery riots. See Patricia Spencer-Silver (1993) *Pugin's Builder, The Life and Work of George Myers*, Hull University Press: 108.

The doors and doorways in the Hospital are very significant to the overall atmosphere and experience of the building: originally religious texts were hand-painted over the doorways, and the fixings for the bell-pulls at each of the entrances remind us that the Hospital used to be more Convent-like than it is now: imagine reaching for the bell-pull, and waiting; waiting, and being ushered in.

But these materials had to be made, hewn, carved, and transported, and this was a period of excitement and militancy for those who worked in the construction industry. On the one hand, the great pioneers and philanthropists desperately needed the skills of those working in the trade: Myers' company alone constructed or restored ninety churches between 1842 and 1873 and also worked on many other civic projects, building three lunatic asylums, including Broadmoor, several hospitals including the Herbert Hospital, whose plans were approved by Florence Nightingale, and offices, banks and warehouses. Myers supported the Architectural Museum in Cannon Row which was established in 1853 'to enable the working man who cannot go in his working dress to museums contained in palaces and marble halls,' to study architecture in an atmosphere where he could feel more at home. He urged upon his own masons the importance of education so that they would be able to 'carry out the spirit of the drawing rather than be content with a mere mechanical execution.'[136]

On the other hand, more than twenty years after Engels' dramatic exposure of *The Condition of the Working Class in England*[137] working people were still expected to surrender most of their waking hours in order to earn a basic wage. Many Master Builders worked fifteen or sixteen hours a day: one builder's son wrote a letter to *The Builder* saying that he and his father rose at 4.45am to start work, often not finishing their estimates, planning and writing until 10 or 10.30pm, and they didn't even know whether they could pay their men at the end of the week especially if employers were cavalier about paying up. On top of their working day men might be walking one or two hours to and from work. Children were still working, legally or illegally, in the brickyards, with nine and ten year-old boys and girls carrying 40lb of clay on their heads. The first Royal Commission of the Trades Unions was making its investigations at this very time, 1867-69. Conflict and changing legislation rendered building an unstable industry, in which only the most financially astute builders were able to operate.

---

[136] Ibid: 90.

[137] Frederick Engels (1844). Engels died near Eastbourne and his ashes were scattered from Beachy Head in

This was also a period of great engineers: in the early 1880s the Hospital installed a water lift, described by one historian as 'a unique piece of Victorian engineering'.[138] The only evidence of the lift now is a couple of otherwise inexplicable holes in the top floor ceiling, some ironwork on the roof, and the recollections of an auxiliary who worked at the Hospital between 1938 and 1958, stating that the lift was on the men's side of the Hospital, it had wooden doors and ropes, and that you had to be extremely strong to operate it.

'The answer to hospital mortality is not prayer but better ventilation, cleanliness, good drainage and good food.'[139] As 'no expense was spared' it is likely that the Hospital also enjoyed state-of-the-art drainage, heating and ventilation systems, especially as two All Saints Sisters were involved in the work of Chorlton Workhouse, Manchester in the 1860s, where the infirmary's ventilation system was largely due to the builders' consultation with Florence Nightingale. These complex systems had to be constructed, of course, and one can only imagine the labour of the thousands of workmen employed over twelve years on the Hospital, its outbuildings and lodges and the Chapel.

ENTRANCE HALL - ALL SAINTS' HOSPITAL

---

[138] Robert Armstrong (1990) *Guide to Eastbourne*, Sound Forum Publications: 42.
[139] Florence Nightingale, c.1861, paraphrased in Spencer-Silver, op.cit: 146.

VII
The waters of healing: the work and life of
All Saints Convalescent Hospital

'those devoted women…are now ready to bring you those waters of healing which are ever vibrating to the angels' touch, and the virtues of which no sufferers can exhaust…'[140]

'the arduous work which the Mothers and Sisters of the hospital had to perform, and…nothing but the love of God could induce them to undertake such an arduous task.'[141]

'he who worked, worshipped' [142]

All Saints Convalescent Hospital was unusual amongst the All Saints Sisters of the Poor's many institutions in that that its work was carried out mainly by Lay Sisters (often former ward nurses) even though Lay Sisters constituted less than 10% of the Sisterhood. It appears that about twelve Lay Sisters worked with between three and eight Choir Sisters, most of whom were Novices, and a number of maids (penitents, mainly responsible for the laundry and other domestic work), under the supervision of the Sister Superior and Sisters-in-Charge. As Sister Elspeth recorded: 'All the Lay Sisters liked Eastbourne…they had good quarters and responsible work.'[143]

A copy of the 1869 Conveyance of the 'Equity of Redemption of the Hospital Buildings and Land at Eastbourne Sussex in Trust for the Charitable purposes within mentioned' gives us a clear idea of how the Hospital was initially operated regarding the Medical Officers, the Patients, the Subscribers and the Donors. Firstly it asked that there be two or more Honorary Physicians, at least one of which should reside in London. The duty of the London Physician was to see London patients at 82 Margaret Street on Tuesdays and Fridays and determine their

---

[140] A London Physician, in a Letter to the Editor, *The Times*, 1869 or 1870.
[141] From a speech by Lady Fanny Howard at the Laying of All Saints Hospital foundation stone, reported in *Eastbourne Gazette*, 24th July 1867.
[142] Reverend T.Lowe, ibid.
[143] Mumm (1999): 46.

suitability as Eastbourne convalescents; and the duty of the other Physician was to attend the Eastbourne Hospital for the medical, surgical and sanitary treatment of the patients. At this time, Walter Rickards, MD and George Augustus Jeffery had consented to jointly accept the appointment of Honorary Physician, with Arthur Whitefield as Honorary Surgeon and a Dispenser.

The Schedule shows that some conditions rendered patients ineligible for care at All Saints: children under two years; anyone beyond the first stage of pulmonary consumption; people recovering from smallpox, typhus or any contagious disease;[144] epileptics; persons of immoral character; and anyone previously guilty of misconduct at the Hospital. To determine eligibility, all patients had to provide a medical certificate stating fully the nature and cause of their disease, approved by the London physician, and

'with the exception of these 6 cases persons to whom change of air is essential for recovery but who still require nursing and care surgical cases still under treatment persons requiring bracing and preparation to enable them to undergo operations…all other convalescents and incurables whether coming from London or any part of the country are eligible as patients without favour or distinction of Creed.'

Some of the newspaper reports also state that All Saints was built for 'incurables' as well as convalescents, and Sister Hildegard mentions incurable boys and men arriving at the Hospital, but Sister says in her 'Memories' that 'a man named Carr and Tourncy a crippled boy were sent [to Eastbourne]…It was intended to have Incurables, as well as Convalescents at the Hospital, but it did not answer.'[145] There is also evidence that some 'incurable' boys were cared for in the 'Home Boys' Wing' (see later section on St. Luke's Children's Hospital).

Initially there were four large 'Nightingale' wards, including, in fact, a ward for incurables and two small rooms for patients requiring special treatment.[146] Florence Nightingale had advocated large open wards not so much for medical reasons as to ensure the safety of her

---

[144] However, a note in the <u>Minutes of the Hospital Advisory Committee</u> for 13th September 1893 recommends that a spare ward to be kept in cases of infectious diseases, and beds to be disinfected after patient has left, using sulphur – at 1.5lbs to 1000cu.ft – and not carbolic, which was a failure.

[145] S. Catherine Williams, in Mumm (2001): 57.

[146] Mayhew, op.cit: 118, and *Eastbourne Chronicle* 24th July 1869.

nurses, who would be vulnerable in a small ward containing recovering soldiers. The design also facilitates surveillance, which at All Saints is perhaps uniquely served by each ward's turreted surveillance room, reached by 'helical' stairs. Photographs of the wards from the Hospital's time as a Canadian Military Hospital and postcards from the 1920s show the wards with sparkling polished oak floors, palms, wood-burning stoves in the centre, iron beds covered in white bedspreads, and all bathed in beautiful light from the tall windows.

The Hospital was supported by voluntary subscription, in a system by which a Subscriber paying £1.1.0 annually would be entitled to one 'Letter' admitting one patient free for a three-week period of convalescence. Should the patient require a longer stay, a payment of nine shillings could be made, or sometimes another Subscribers' Letter would allow for another three weeks' stay. A donation of £10.10.0 in one sum would entitle the donor during his life to such a Letter yearly. All Annual Subscriptions would become due in June or December and were paid in advance. However, patients had to provide for their own washing and travelling expenses.[147] Patients requiring a private ward had to pay one guinea weekly in advance but would have to take their meals with the other patients during the day. All patients had to bind themselves to submit to the Government and Discipline of the Hospital 'on pain of expulsion.' The Rules, pinned up on the wall and noted down by the Canadian Captain Seaborn in 1917 (and one suspects had not changed very much since 1869) are as follows:[148]

Rules for All Saints Convalescent Hospital, Eastbourne – Women

As the Divine Blessing cannot be expected for the recovery of health without prayer, the Inmates of this hospital will be required to attend Morning and Evening Prayers, and the Services of the Chapel on Sunday.

As Persons of all Creeds are received, it is especially desired that no religious arguments or controversy should take place and no Patient may lend a Book to another without the permission of the Sister of her ward.

---

[147] A deal was made in 1880 with the London Brighton & South Coast Railway Company so that patients could first of all travel third class at cheaper rates, then in 1888 they were able to travel second class at third class prices, subject to the Hospital guaranteeing a minimum number of travellers per year: Minutes of the Hospital Advisory Committee, December 1880 and June & November 1888.

[148] I have taken the liberty of changing the order of these Rules to show the significance of the *religious* management of the institution.

Silence must be observed in the Wards after 8.30 p.m. and until 8 a.m. and always on the stairs and passages and at meals.

Should any Inmates show discontent or disobedience to the Superior Sisters or Nurse, manifest an unloving temper to her companions or in any respect show an unwillingness to observe the Rules of the Hospital, she will be required to leave at once, that the law of love may not be broken, where all are called upon to bear one another's burdens.

The hour for rising will be 7.30 a.m. unless permission is given to the contrary, and all must be in bed by 9.15 p.m. in the summer and 9 in the winter, when the lights will be put out.

No cooking of any kind allowed either in the Wards or Sitting Room.

No Wines or Spirits to be purchased by the Patients or brought into the House and any Patients seen going into a <u>Public House or heard of there, will be instantly dismissed.</u>

No Books or Newspapers to be brought into the House without first being shown to the Superior and approved by her.

No patient to change her bed, or take Pillows or bolsters from other beds or to open or shut windows.

The patients are not to go into each other's Wards or about the Hospital without leave.

All are to remain in the Sitting Room during the day, unless they have permission to the contrary.

The Patients must ask permission before going out, and all must return at the hour specified.

The doors of the wards and Sitting Room are to be kept shut.

Each inmate to make her own Bed, and all to assist one another as much as possible, and to help in any way they can for the benefit of the Institution according to the direction of the Superior.

No patient having once been discharged for misconduct will <u>ever again</u> be received into the institution.

No Patient is allowed to bathe without first having obtained the sanction of the Visiting Physician.

The Patients must leave their sitting rooms perfectly neat before going out, or going to bed; and no sea-weed, stones, etc. are allowed to be brought into the hospital.

Any Patient found in the apartments allotted to the men, or holding any conversation with them about the hospital or Garden or elsewhere will be liable to instant dismissal.

The Patients are not allowed to go out in a boat without special leave.

Despite having a turnover of 1,000 and 3,000 patients each year, the Hospital was able to accommodate all manner of guests: in July 1874, just after the Chapel was opened, the poet Christina Rossetti wrote to her publisher, Alexander Macmillan:

'Do you know anything of this grand Hospital where my Mother & I are staying? We, of course, as paying visitors: but (say) 200 other poor people, convalescents, enjoying all comforts within this magnificent house, & without superb sea & downs to their hearts' content. This is truly a noble institution, worthy of support on all hands as patients are admitted to it from all parts,—& reflecting high honour on its Foundress.'[149]

Christina and her mother were of course visiting Sister Maria Francesca Rossetti who was at this time seriously ill and was being nursed at the Hospital. Although she recovered enough to continue her Novitiate, Sister Maria was sent again to Eastbourne in 1876 suffering from cancer, where she was cared for by 'little young Nurse Annie' who had been trained at University College Hospital and was the wife of the Hospital steward, Mr. Gerard. Sister Maria was always calling Annie to her bedside 'in her Italian ecstatic way "Oh Annie, my Annie, come to me!" Maria's was a 'very suffering death'[150] on 24th November 1876. About her sister's funeral, Christina Rossetti wrote:

'And at a moment which was sad only for us who lost her, all turned out in harmony with her holy hope and joy. Flowers covered her, loving mourners followed her, hymns were sung at her grave, the November day brightened, and the sun...made a miniature rainbow in my eyelashes.'[151]

The Hospital accommodated not only all these patients, the Sisters and domestic staff, and visitors who paid for a private room, but was also frequented by other religious communities, in particular the Society of St. John the Evangelist. Friends of the Sisters were welcome too: Sister Catherine Williams remembers that when Mother Foundress made her own frequent stays at the Hospital (apparently 'never so happy as when there'),[152] the two small children of the Reverend Arthur Brinkman often visited and used to run in and out of Mother's room and over the whole place as they liked.'[153]

---

[149]Letter dated 27th July 1874, in Anthony H. Harrison, ed (1999), *The Letters of Christina Rossetti*, Vol.2 1874-1881, The University Press of Virginia: 19.

[150] S. Caroline Mary, in Mumm (2001): 32.

[151] Cited in Battiscombe, op.cit: 159.

[152] Mumm (2001): 61.

[153] Ibid.

In addition to those working with patients inside the Hospital, there were many manual workers attached to the Hospital, some of whom lived in a row of cottages between Darley Road and the Ship Inn, known as All Saints Cottages. At the Hospital gate house in Darley Road lived Stewart Thorpe who used to drive a governess cart drawn by a donkey between the Hospital and the railway station, and later there was 'a private omnibus with one horse to take patients…& an old coachman…followed by a splendid St. Bernard's dog, "Chad", a great pet.'[154] There were also stewards, gardeners, cooks, maintenance workers and the Resident Engineer. The institution was expected to be almost self sufficient, and the gardeners worked kitchen gardens in the Hospital grounds and grew potatoes on additional land bought between the Hospital and the sea until it was let as a school playing field. The gardens were unlikely to have provided the 'Apples and quinces,/Lemons and oranges,/ Plump unpecked cherries,/Melons and raspberries,/Bloom-down-cheeked peaches,/Swart-headed mulberries,/Wild free-born cranberries' of Christina Rossetti's startling poem 'Goblin Market' (1862) but there was an orchard at the west end of the Hospital, and one of the outbuildings was an apple store. The other outbuildings were stables, the laundry and a mortuary.

When Sister Catherine Williams started work at Eastbourne in 1871 after a time at University College Hospital, she had entire charge of the boys, took the men's meals, dressed their wounds and did what nursing was required. Sister Constance welcomed the patients when they arrived, and lent them books. 'We had pigeons and rabbits in the old garden [Mother Foundress's religious garden] which I looked after with the Server's help (Fred Rupp). The boys were in S. Stanislas Ward and the girls in S. Ursula. S. Rose ward and the men's library were not yet built.'[155] In 1887 a new wing was opened, in harmony with the rest of the building, and with an excellent view of Beachy Head. The Hospital now contained 275 beds, and had received 2,870 patients that year, which meant more work for the Sisters, but the new wing provided an extra thirty beds, helping to reduce the waiting time of eight or nine weeks for those 'poor and forlorn of London' who would – in the words of an eminent surgeon – 'not get better unless he is taken to Eastbourne', to the flowers in the spring, the chalk cliffs, the pebbly beach.[156]

---

[154] Ibid.
[155] Cited in Mumm (2001): 61
[156] From article in *The Times*, date unknown.

In 1869 Sister Anne - the first Sister Superior of All Saints Convalescent Hospital - was responsible for all this astonishing care. Sister Anne remained Sister Superior until she died in 1918, after nearly fifty years of managing the Hospital from its grand, pioneering start to the beginning of a wholly different era. Recalling her colleague in the early days at Margaret Street, Sister Caroline Mary says

'When I entered the Novitiate, Sister Anne was a young Professed and used to <u>Dispense</u> with a Novice under her, and was also Sacristan of the Chapel and very often I saw her carrying up two buckets of water, one in each hand, up the crooked steps (then) to the Chapel. She would wash the whole Chapel herself. Though always the same slight figure, she had great muscular strength. As soon as Convalescent work began at Eastbourne, Mother Foundress had her down there – and prepared her to become the first Sister Superior as soon as the large Hospital was completed and opened.'[157]

Sister Rosamund Buckley was also at Eastbourne from the beginning: she was described as 'saintly.' Professed in her forties, this was the woman who insisted on living like the paupers in the Manchester Workhouse Infirmary. She had also trained at University College Hospital, and she was a talented artist, painting all the first big texts put up over the doors of the wards and the iron balustrades of the great staircases. She died working in Bombay 1879 where the All Saints Sisters were called to teach in girls' schools.

Whilst Mother Foundress presided over the design, building and establishment of the Convalescent Hospital, she was also arranging and overseeing new All Saints Sisters missions in Capetown, South Africa and Baltimore, America, as well as India, and all over Britain: the Sisters established girls' schools and orphanages, an institute for the sons of colliers in Leeds, homes for people who were aged or infirm. Not only did this involve astute business sense, Mother Foundress also offered continuous pastoral care to her Sisters, writing to them all over the world, admonishing them, sending them love and small gifts. She also understood the value of rest and recreation, however, and one of her greatest delights at Eastbourne was a garden she had bought in Meads, which she used as a religious sanctuary.

---

[157] Mumm (2001): 17.

'the beautiful old Walled-in Garden Foundress Mother was able to purchase and add to our Community portion of the Hospital. This garden has been made and lived in by an eccentric old man who lived on its fruits and vegetables. He planted many rare trees and when he died, it was to be put up for sale by auction, but our F. Mother was able to purchase it privately and she made it into a thorough Religious Garden with a Calvary and Shrines for Our Lady and St. Aloysius and there was *then* a beautiful cloistered walk of trees meeting overhead and the stillness and quiet beauty was most helpful to any Novices or visiting Sisters for reading or meditations. On Sundays, Mother often took Recreation there – both for Choir and Lay Sisters and Novices. We used to sit on the grass all around her seat…The S.S.J.E. Fathers …were sent…to 'rest' at our Eastbourne Hospital, or to act as Chaplain, whilst the Resident Chaplain was away for *his* 'rest.' The Fathers used to use our Cloistered Garden at times when the Sisters were not likely to be there. Fr. Prescott was especially fond of walking up and down the walk with trees meeting overhead, reading his Breviary.'[158]

In 1871 Mother Foundress had purchased Robert Caldecott's garden, complete with folly, in Meads Street. It has been described as a 'huge excavation some 30 yards long, half as wide and sloping to a depth of 15' in the middle…[with] a mound nearly 30' high which rises up steeply from the south side of the dingle. Built against the perimeter of the mound there is over 30 yards of wall composed of flint, mortar and brick. It rises to a height of 30 feet along much of its length and includes an arch, an observation turret, two small chambers, one above the other, projecting from the wall and a small shrine or grotto. The latter is approached by five stone steps and has a floor of coloured tiles. Against the back wall is a low 'altar' of concrete moulded in imitation of stone cobbles….It is difficult to conceive what purpose these constructions were intended to serve.'[159]

These and other complex constructions and excavations (with the possible exception of parts of the shrines) were the work of a man known as 'eccentric, quiet, unassuming and well-meaning gentleman [who] forsook college life in Oxford to settle in Meads…to get away from the slavery of fashion.' He was a strict churchman and almost monastic in his habits. It was his custom frequently to retire to his mounds and walls for long periods of meditation, clad, it is said, in a nightshirt. Strict churchman he may have been but it is reported that at church he had been in the habit of taking off his boots during the service and even on occasion changing his clothes - he sorely missed the old-fashioned box pews that had been swept away in the church building of the Gothic Revival.[160] The garden was sold off in February 1957 for £4,000 together with a strip of land that continued to be used by the Hospital Kitchen garden.

---

[158] Sister Caroline Mary, in Mumm (2001): 26-7.

[159] F.G.Heys, 'Caldecott's Folly,' *Eastbourne Local History Newsletter,* No.30, 1978: 4.

[160] 'Note of the Life and Customs of Robert Marriott Caldecott - the Planter of Mother's Garden ' (anon) in All Saints Convent Archives, Oxford. At his death in 1871, Caldecott bequeathed to the town his geological collection, housed at the Caldecott Museum, Lismore Road (thought destroyed in World War II). The collection held 1,700 rocks and minerals, 1,300 local fossils and 1,900 fossils from elsewhere, shells, lichens and sponges; birds, including a buzzard, a gyr falcon and puffins; saurian teeth and petrified bones of the iguanodon, crystals (geode) and gems; also antlers, and the tooth of a rhinoceros picked up in an excavation of South Street.

VIII
St. Luke's Children's Hospital –
The Harriet Brownlow Memorial

'On September 1ˢᵗ the house was taken, so that she might begin a life of separation
<u>from her home</u> and from the world: so it came to pass that on
St. Luke's Day 1851 our Foundress <u>left her home'</u>[161]

'very soon, after our Mother Foundress'ss death, the desire to erect a Memorial worthy of her, began to take shape, and after great meetings of influential and old friends of the Community, it was decided to build the Children's Hospital at Eastbourne on the site of the Coast Guard Cottages which had been bought and used for little girls' convalescence. Convalescent boys, at that time, were in St. Stanislas Ward in the Adult Hospital.

Much time had to be given with Sister Anne, over the plans for the Memorial, and the Architect, Mowbray of Oxford, carried out Sister Anne's desires and suggestions very thoroughly.

The first stone of the Memorial was laid by the Duchess of Albany on July 19, 1888. It was a beautiful day and the choirboys from All Saints came down under their priest in charge, Mr. Ward. Their blue cassocks and white cottas and the processional cross glimmering in the sun looked a bright picture as they led the procession from the Hospital to the platform for the laying of the first stone.

Numbers of old friends and All Saints people were there. Afterwards there was a luncheon for the Princess-Duchess, and Dr. Frank who had known her when she was a child, sat beside her. She told us that her little son, the Duke of Albany – born after his father Prince Leopold's death - was four years old that day.'[162]

---

[161] Sister Elspeth, in Mumm (2001): 188. On the same day, the Prince and Princess also formally opened the new children's wing at the Princess Alice Hospital.

[162] 'Memories of Sister Caroline Mary,' ibid: 41. Dr. Frank worked with the Sisters in the Franco-Prussian War.

St. Luke's Children's Hospital

St. Luke's at that time took over one hundred 'delicate and convalescent' children of ages between 3 and 16, with five beds for mothers with infants under six months,[163] although sources vary. In a contemporary letter to *The Times* a Mr. G. Salisbury appealed for donations so that St. Luke's could be built:

'Sir, - To all those who have the interest of suffering children and their convalescence from illness at heart, we make a most earnest appeal for funds to raise a new hospital for convalescent children at Eastbourne, on the site of the small adapted building now in use, which is quite inadequate to the present needs [the Coast Guard Cottages], and where we are able to receive but a very few of those who apply for admittance.

Children can be received from 4-14 years, and it is to secure a proper building with all the modern sanitary improvements and large enough for the purpose that we now ask your aid.' [164]

Over the door of the new hospital were the words: *'1889 This hospital for children is erected to the glory of God, in loving memory of Harriet Brownlow Byron, foundress of the All Saints Community of the Sisters of the Poor 1851.'* Also above the entrance were a group of carved figures, the Good Shepherd, St. Michael and St. Gabriel. Inside, the wards were named after Saints - Elizabeth, Gertrude, Raphael and others. The girls' playroom was apparently a

'pleasant chamber with magnificent sea views, placed under the protection of "The Holy Guardian Angels"…Internally the arrangements seem simply perfect, and, for brightness, pleasantness and utility, leave nothing to be desired….The new building, which will give accommodation to 130 beds, is of red brick with blue reliefs and red tiled roof, and has cost £10,000. It is heated by steam, and perfectly ventilated, while cheery day rooms, covered playground, and comfortable dormitories, combined with the pleasant scenic surroundings, will make this, indeed, a home as well as a hospital, for the children of the poor from all parts of the kingdom. This loving tribute to the memory of a good and self-sacrificing woman should, though supported by voluntary contributions, never want for funds.'[165]

---

[163] Published by the British Medical Association at Eastbourne, July 1931: 100-101.

[164] *The Times,* (exact date unknown).

[165] Ibid.

The architect this time was Mr. A. Marden Mowbray, FRIBA, who practiced both in Oxford and Eastbourne. We know from Minutes of the Hospital Advisory Committee in 1883, however, that earlier Henry Woodyer had asked for £200 commission for 'Drawings' he made for a boys' hospital at an estimated cost of £8,000, claiming two and a half per cent on that amount 'for Drawings only'[166]. An architect's standard fee at this time was apparently 5% of the building cost, and it was normal practice for Woodyer to be paid half this fee if he provided drawings, even if the building did not proceed. Woodyer's request for payment could indicate that the architect 'was irritated with the way the Committee was handling the matter – 'there's some evidence that Woodyer disliked dealing with committees…and might well have …asked to be paid as a way of terminating his commission.'[167]

St. Luke's was requisitioned during the First and Second World Wars (see below) and later opened to old and infirm women and men. After the second war it was handed back to the Sisters still occupied by some aged patients and it was proposed that the Children's Hospital should now be used only for the old and infirm – to be reopened January 1946 as a Hospital for Adults. The Sister-in-Charge at St. Luke's for a number of years was Sister Bridget.[168] Sister Bridget had served in the Church Army in India, and had been professed in the All Saints Indian Affiliation. After leaving India she continued to suffer frequent bouts of malaria. She is described as having 'quite a bark, but a heart of gold.' She certainly had some eccentric ways: it is said that she kept a pet rat on her desk and was buried with her parrot; and that when two fishmongers were accepted for the hospital she had fresh fish sent in for their breakfast every day.[169] At the request of the Police Sister Bridget frequently took people in from the streets, some of whom, men as well as women, were in poor condition, some even needing to learn how to bath themselves.

In 1960, after the Sisters had ceased to manage the two Hospitals, the National Health Service purchased St. Luke's, which was then put up for auction, and its description here gives us most of what we know about the building, which contained 'seventeen large wards or

---

[166] Minute of the All Saints Convalescent Hospital Advisory Committee 22nd February 1883.
[167] John Pritchard, in correspondence with the author: 22nd March 2002.
[168] Mayhew, op.cit: 123-4.
[169] Ibid: 124.

communal rooms, thirty-nine other rooms, extensive service, catering, administrative and storage accommodation including extensive, excellent, up-to-date toilet accommodation, two lifts and comprehensive oil-fired central heating…

Lower ground floor: Sisters' Refectory, Patients' Dining Room, 5 Toilets, two small staff rooms, sisters' sitting room, kitchen, large scullery, Sisters' China Pantry with sinks, store rooms, two further toilets, staff bedroom, priests' room, further bedroom. '

Ground floor: hall and vestibule, seven wards or large rooms, one of the largest being used as a Chapel, ten smaller rooms (used as Office, Dispensary and Private Wards), seven toilets

First floor: six wards or large rooms, eight smaller rooms.

Second floor: Seven rooms, bathroom, two bedrooms with separate stairs. Large loft. Garden lodge, tool shed and fruit store. Good garden. Frontage c.460."[170]

The freehold, vacant possession and nearly two acres of land were bought by A. J. Wait & Co. Ltd, New Malden for £75,000, who had earlier sought and obtained outline planning permission for the demolition of the property and erection of flats – surely not what the Sisters would have wanted for the Memorial of their beloved Mother Foundress. St. Luke's was demolished later that year, 1960; Dolphin Court, a block of flats was opened on the site in 1965.

The Home Boys' Wing

In 1919 seriously ill boys who had been nursed by the Sisters in a house called 'The Incurable Boys' Home,' were moved to Eastbourne first of all to St. Luke's and then to the 'Home Boys' Wing' in the main Hospital. Some of the boys were able to attend local schools, and could eventually go back to their London homes. For delicate boys the Sisters made careful attempts to find them suitable employment.[171] The Report for 1919 for the All Saints Boys' Home gives a short history of the Home:

'This work was begun about 40 years ago by the Foundress Mother of the All Saints Community. The first abode was at St. Elizabeth's Home for old and infirm women in Mortimer Street, where one ward was set apart for six little boys who were thought to be

---

[170] <u>Particulars, Conditions of Sale and Plan</u>, February 1960.
[171] All in Mayhew, p.122-3

incurable. In later years the work was moved to 4 Margaret Street, and in 1898 the House was entirely rebuilt.

...since in these days very few cases are really incurable, especially among children, the word was considered a misnomer, and so the name was changed to "All Saints Boys' Home".

The boys who are taken are children between the ages of two and fourteen, who are not ill enough for treatment in Hospital and are unable to receive the necessary care and attention in their own homes. Properly looked after and well fed, they grow up bright and fairly strong, able to earn their own living, and to become good and useful men.

The Home, small as it is, supplies a veritable need. We try to make it a *real home* for the boys, and not merely an institution. They go to the ordinary school, they join as far as they can in games and exercises with other boys, and nothing strikes visitors more than their superabundance of energy and high spirits. What is most important of all – they are brought up as Catholics from their earliest days, and watched over with the greatest care during the important period of school life...

At present, owing to the delay caused by difficulty in obtaining material and labour, we are still in temporary quarters at the Children's Hospital; but when the buildings are finished the plan is to move the children into a wing of the large Hospital, which will keep them separate from convalescent children coming from London...'[172]

The boys were suffering such conditions as spinal deformity, caused by tuberculous disease of the spine after an attack of the measles; another had diptheria and subsequently a tracheotomy; another fell out of a wheelbarrow at age five, causing damage to the upper spine. He lived in a Phelps's spinal box for a year, and was then put in a poroplastic jacket with head support and could get up and go to school. Another had bone damage in one of his legs caused by TB, and another had lost an arm and suffered serious head injury when he was knocked down by an army lorry close to the Queen Alexander Military Hospital in 1918, aged seven.

The cost of caring for these boys greatly exceeded the institution's income, despite subscriptions amounting to £75.5.0 pa and donations of £490.19.8 plus fundraising efforts of various kinds, and in November 1946 the Boys' Home assets were transferred to the main Hospital.

---

[172] *Annual Report of the Home Boys' Wing* (1919), All Saints Convalescent Hospital, Eastbourne; Chaplain The Reverend G. Budibent.

VIX
The 10th Canadian Military Unit
Eastbourne

Between 1899 and 1945 three wars affected the life of All Saints Convalescent Hospital. In June 1899 the All Saints Hospital Committee resolved that because of the present war in South Africa the Hospital would set apart thirty beds for the reception of convalescent soldiers, sick or wounded, 'charge reduced to £1.11.0 per man and can stay longer than three weeks.' The Committee duly informed the Soldiers' and Sailors' Help Society that ten of the beds were for the Guards Brigade Committee (but no man could stay longer than two months). Perhaps this explains the fact that in May 1900 'Meads Village was gaily decorated to celebrate the relief of Mafeking'[173] although we have no evidence so far that these soldiers did in fact stay at the Hospital. We do know, however, that All Saints was taken over by the 10th Canadian Military Unit in 1917.

'In May and June 1917 the sound of cannonading in France could be most distinctly heard. At the time of the great Canadian attack on Messines Ridge the explosions were so loud and distinct that many were awakened out of good sleep.'[174]

Several years ago All Saints Hospital received a letter from Martha Walcot in Ontario, whose father, Private William Worth Davis, had been stationed at All Saints Convalescent Hospital in 1917 when it was taken over for use as a Canadian Military Hospital and the Sisters were dispatched to lodgings nearby. During his time there Davis, an optician, made a lens from a pair of spectacles and built it into a homemade box, enabling him to take photographs. Photographing military property or activity was of course strictly illegal and would have resulted in court martial had he been discovered. Due to his reckless courage and ingenuity, we have now a photographic record of the life of All Saints throughout 1917, and thanks to Martha Walcot we also have a history of the 10th Canadian Stationary Hospital written by Dr. Edwin

---

[173] Gausden, op.cit:
[174] Dr.Edwin Seaborn, 'Number Ten Stationary Hospital' (undated): 23.

Seaborn, who was at that time a Lieutenant Colonel and Principal Medical Officer on H.M. Troopship 2810, and on the Board of Trustees to whom the records of the 10th Unit were handed over in 1919.

Between 1914 and 1916 the Medical Faculty of the Western University of Canada made several offers to the Canadian Government to organize a complete hospital unit for overseas service. Finally the Unit was mobilized as No.10 Stationary Hospital, Canadian Expeditionary Force, on 28th April 1916, arriving in Liverpool on 30th August. The Unit was initially encamped at Shorncliffe, Kent and after further training, took over the Ravenscroft Military Hospital at Seaford on 5th November 1916. Seaford had been chosen for a training camp at the beginning of the war, and many troops from India had been quartered there - 'The rolling downs are excellent for camp purposes'[175] - and by the time the 10th Unit arrived, there were already 12,000 Canadian troops. These men had come directly from overseas and because of the confinement on the boat and changes in climatic and other conditions, there was a great deal of sickness, such that another 100 beds were taken at Seaside Convalescent Hospital in Brighton and the Unit also took over two private schools, in Seaford, 'Southlands' and 'Hawkswick.'[176] Amongst the troops were epidemics of cerebro-spinal fever (meningitis), scarlet fever, diptheria, measles and mumps.

By May 1916 there were just twenty-two patients left in All Saints and later these civilian patients were moved to an empty girls' school in Bolsover Road. All Saints was then equipped and staffed by the Canadians to take a maximum of 700 cases.[177] On 31st December 1916 arrangements began for the taking over of All Saints,' and the Unit, consisting of fourteen Officers, one Matron and twenty-six nursing sisters, and 118 other ranks, took possession of the Convalescent Hospital on 21st January 1917. Seaborn writes that the All Saints Sisters

'felt the separation from their old Hospital very keenly but showed a most admirable spirit of self-sacrifice. The Sister Superior had lived there for more than 60 years.[178] They showed

---

[175] Ibid: 8.

[176] The Seaford Camps were major training centres for forestry corps, railway construction battalions and engineer and infantry units. R.A. Elliston (1999), *Eastbourne's Great War 1914-18*, SB Publications: 39.

[177] Ibid: 25.

[178] Seaborn is referring to Sister Anne who had indeed been Sister Superior since 1869. However, the Convalescent Hospital had only been running for only 48 years by 1917.

Photographs from Pte.Worth Davis' All Saints album, 1917-18

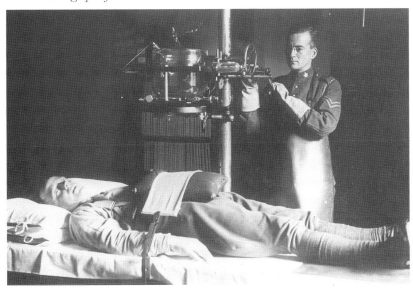

unfailing courtesy and made our patients many donations of fruit and vegetables from the gardens.[179] They moved to a large private house and there continued their charitable work.'[180]

Seaborn continues with a description of the Hospital as it was in 1917:

'The two stone stairways are of light construction and all note the beauty of the flying stairs. Pillared balcony at each end overlook the gardens, cricket grounds, the town, and the sea. The view is exceptionally beautiful. From the middle of the building projects…the cloisters of the Sisters, afterwards the quarters of our Nursing Sisters. The wards are large, bright and airy, and are heated by hot water from a central furnace. In all the wards there are large grates and bright fires. Beyond the main building project others, forming a court and containing the Nursing Sisters' Mess, Officers' Anteroom and Mess, Men's recreation room, canteen and linen room. The linen room was already well arranged and by the addition of shelving holds all the linen of the hospital. The kitchens are old but good and the cooking is done by steam from a stationary boiler. We have added an army range to its equipment. The patients' dining room is used for concerts and church services. On the west of the court are hospital wards and a large archway. Beyond are the stables, which we used for rough storage. It was necessary to remodel parts of the building for X-Ray, Operating and Pathology Rooms, and to improve the heating, lighting and water supply and the drainage.

The second building, known as "The Children's" [St. Luke's] we renamed "The Lady Beck Building" in honour of the President of the Red Cross Society of London,[181] it overlooks the sea. Nothing intervenes but the "King Edward Parade." Here the rooms are not very large but are well adapted to our use. We have taken over the furniture as well as the buildings. The beds were not sufficiently good for the use of the wounded and were replaced by hospital cots. Our personnel used the beds and furnished with mattresses, are very comfortable indeed. Our personnel are housed at the top of the main and Lady Beck buildings and above their recreation room.'[182]

---

[179] Sister Hildegard describes the Canadians, however, as 'very rough.' Sister Hildegard, op.cit: 5.

[180] Seaborn, op.cit: 13.

[181] Lady Beck and Mrs. C.R. Somerville, directing the London Branch of the Canadian Red Cross Society, 'most generously furnished dressings and other necessaries,' working 13-hour days to provide the equipment for the Unit within 4 weeks of the request. Seaborn: 6.

[182] Ibid: 15-16.

During this period the chief expenditures of the Unit were for equipment for the X-ray department, the Laboratory and Quartermaster; and a little for additional food or comforts for patients, or materials and tools for the carpenter and plumber. Apparatus for blood transfusions was presented by the Dean of the Medical Faculty, the first successful transfusion being for a soldier with acute appendicitis, using blood from two donor patients within the Hospital. Supplies sent down by the Canadian Red Cross in London initially included 1,224 Abdominal Binders, 10,000 gauze sponges, 1,012 Helpless Shirts, 3,096 Cheese Cloth Hankies, 324 Fomentation Wringers, 524 Hot Water Bottle Covers, 500 Stump Dressings, and 144 Laparatomy Stockings.[183]

The hospital was purely for Canadian patients, from the Seaford camp and from overseas via the Imperial hospitals. All Canadian patients in other Eastbourne hospitals were transferred to All Saints before definite discharge.100 beds were set aside as an invaliding section for serious cases, some of whom had been in Imperial hospitals for many months.

'We found it a difficult and often disagreeable duty to distinguish malingering and functional or organic diseases. Mention is made of the work of Captain E.H. Young, specialist in mental and nervous diseases. Many obstinate cases recovered. A department of mechano-therapeutics was installed in the "Lady Beck Building". Captain Young designed simple but effective apparatus and these were made by our carpenter from materials provided from the Emergency Fund.'[184]

The X-ray department was under the supervision of Captain E. Bice, whose plates were said to be of an exceptionally high quality; in Pathology equipment was provided for the Wasserman Test (for syphilis) and other tests from the Emergency Fund; early cytological examination of all wounds was undertaken; a forty-bed Eye department and a dental clinic were also established.

Patients were visited by Reverend F. Pring Rowe, then Chaplain of All Saints and through him many gifts were made, including a piano and a Victrola (an early gramophone). On 1st June 1917, the 50th Anniversary of the founding of the Dominion of Canada, the Canadians held an 'At Hospital' on the athletic field of St. Andrew's School 'for the many people here who had interested themselves in us.' It was apparently a beautiful day, the band of the 6th Canadian

---

[183] Ibid: 6.

[184] Ibid: 21. One wonders by which methods the obstinate cases 'recovered.'

Reserve Battalion played 'O Canada,' some of the Privates sang, and the occasion was attended by, among others, Sir Ernest and Lady Shackleton and the Victoria League. During that summer the Mayor, Mr. J. O'Brien Harding, entertained all the overseas men in Eastbourne: ladies came to the hospital and instructed 'up-patients' in embroidery and other fancy work, some invited small detachments to tea, one man took fifty men to Heathfield in a char-a-banc, and 'prominent men' sent by the Victoria League lectured illustrating their subjects by lantern slides,' including Shackleton on his expedition to the South Pole:

'The description of the hardships and disasters suffered by his men were followed with interest. The story of their bravery and devotion and of their ultimate rescue was most thrilling. This was, I believe, the simplest and most eloquent address I have ever heard. Sir Ernest had not yet delivered a public address on this subject but wished to do this in acknowledgement to Canadians for the many kindnesses they had shown him.'[185]

On 7th November the Duke of Connaught visited the Hospital, commenting on 'the brightness and airiness of the rooms and happy appearance of the patients. He had never visited a hospital that pleased him more, he said.'[186] In fact by this time the whole town had become a big hospital and convalescent centre, with two large hospitals, among others, in Meads, one at De Walden Court, and two large convalescent camps in the Old Town area, known as the 'Summerdown' and 'Cavalry Command' camps. The troops in these camps wore a blue uniform while they were sick and were thus called the 'Blue Boys.' 'Some with terrible wounds and injuries, others with amputations…those that were shell shocked, had fevers, illnesses, trench feet, it was endless, and there were thousands of them.'[187] Those who needed medical care were sent to All Saints, where at least four Canadians died after civilian accidents.[188] According to Seaborn the Unit left Eastbourne for Calais on 4th December 1917 and remained operational there until April 1919.

---

[185] Ibid: 25.

[186] Ibid. Ward tablets in honour of all those who showed an interest in the Unit were temporarily fixed to the walls of the wards of both All Saints and the Seaford hospitals. These tablets were later removed and taken to France. The list of names is given by Seaborn: 11-12.

[187] Douglas Swift, extract from 'Slices of Lives' (c.1991) in *Eastbourne Local History Newsletter,* No. 81, Autumn 1991: 15.

[188] Elliston, op.cit: 93-4.

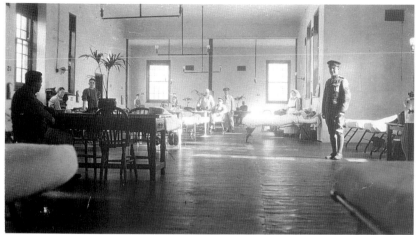 

Military Ward 31

Capt. Douglas, Officer in Charge, Laboratories

What we know about All Saints between the First and Second World Wars comes in part from a conversation between Alice Whitman, who started work as a maid at the Hospital in 1923, most probably working at St. Luke's, and Peter Mayhew, Chaplain to the All Saints Sisters in Oxford 1974-1980:

'She was very small and wore a pinafore instead of an apron. She had learned to sew; she cleaned, and sometimes went out with the young patients. She remembers vividly the 'seventy-six invalid boys and the eighty-six invalid girls.' She was paid £18 per quarter for her work there. She spent her first quarter's pay on the afternoon of the day she received it; she had never before had so much money. She bought a dress for five shillings, a clock for half-a-crown, had tea in Lyons' for sixpence, and went to the pictures for threepence...She did not care much for the cooking at Eastbourne; least of all did she like Sister Lydia's 'Beachy Head Pudding.' She remembers Sister Bridget's tame rat which she kept on her desk. He was called Tommy and had a red collar. People tended to keep away from Sister's desk...'[189]

---

[189] Mayhew, op.cit: 125.

All Saints Convalescent Hospital's entry in the 1931 *The Book of Eastbourne* also gives us an insight into the business of the Hospital at that time. The Hospital was now under the care of four Visiting Physicians, and for each of the three departments (for men, women and children) there was an experienced trained nurse under the supervision of the Visiting Medical Officers. At that time the Hospital was approved by the Ministry of Health for the admission of ambulant non-pulmonary cases of tuberculosis. Patients over 70 years or recovering from infectious or contagious diseases were still ineligible, and patients were expected to be well enough to be up and about during the day and generally able to manage for themselves. 'Bed cases' were ineligible. Patients were sent for convalescence by the chief hospitals both in London and the provinces, by Health Insurance and other charitable societies. Over 3,000 patients were admitted during the course of year. The hospital was open all year round and to patients of all religious denominations.

Although vaccination was not compulsory before admission, the hospital medical officers held themselves 'free to vaccinate any patient in case of emergency.' All children were to obtain a negative result of nasal-throat swab before admission. The current charges were 21s for adults, children aged 12-16 years, 16s, children under 12, 13s 6d. Patients were also still admitted on subscribers' letters. These were issued to regular Annual Subscribers of 21s or more, one letter for each 21s subscribed.

'The Sister Superior, who is responsible for the management of the hospital, realises fully what important factors in convalescence are fresh air, rest, and plentiful nourishing, wholesome food. She and the other Sisters working with her make it their chief aim to give patients such care, sympathy and attention as may help to complete restoration of health…The hospital is open to visitors every afternoon, except Sunday, and the Sisters always welcome visits from those who are interested in the work.'

The Sister Superior referred to here was Sister Mary Theodora, who managed the Hospital between 1919 and her death in 1935. With 'her unflagging zeal and charm [she]…set a shining example to all with whom she came into contact.'[190]

---

[190] These are the words on a Crucifix erected by S. Mary Theodora's friends in All Saints Chapel.

All Saints Hospital during World War II

In March 1937 Sister Ethelburga, now Sister Superior,[191] received the following letter:

Dear Madam,   *16th March 1937*

First-Aid Post and Base Hospital
I have to inform you that the Air Raid Precautions Sub-Committee of the Council have had under consideration the establishment of First-Aid Posts and Base Hospitals in connection with the Scheme for Air Raid Precautions for Eastbourne now in course of preparation. The requirements to which a building proposed to be used as a first-aid post must comply are such that there are very few buildings in the west of the Town which could be utilized for the purpose. It would appear that the All Saints Convalescent Hospital would suit admirably as a first-aid post and also as a Base Hospital. The Sub-Committee, therefore, wish me to enquire whether you would be prepared to allow the Hospital to be earmarked for this purpose.
I should explain that the effect of earmarking the building is that comprehensive plans are prepared for converting the building into a first-aid post, but no steps are taken to put the plans into effect, as such action would only be taken on receipt of information from the Government that hostilities are imminent. etc.etc.

H.W.Fovargue, Town Clerk [Eastbourne][192]

The Committee came up with two proposals in response to this letter, firstly to become a Grade B Hospital and to receive, in cooperation with the A.R.P. Committee 200 adult patients, or secondly to become a Grade A1 Hospital and receive say 700 patients, which would entail the All Saints Sisters vacating the building and evacuating all the convalescent patients. Neither plan was to include St. Luke's Children's Hospital, but structural alterations would have to be made to the adults' hospital. The Committee decided to adopt the first proposal, and the Hospital was taken over in early September 1939 by the Ministry of Health as a Grade B

---

[191] S. Ethelburga was previously Headmistress of the Sisters' St. Peter's Girls School in Khandala, India. She was known for her devotion to duty and as a capable manager.
[192] A letter with the Minutes of the All Saints Convalescent Hospital Advisory Committee, 28th November 1945.

Hospital, and was formally de-requisitioned on 31st July 1945 although after that time there remained a considerable amount of plant to be removed.

Sister Hildegard writes that the Children's Hospital was in fact annexed as well as the main Hospital, taking in people made homeless by the war, and later being occupied by old and infirm men and women. 'It was handed back still with some inmates in it and it was decided to keep it on as a Home for aged and infirm women as there was such a tremendous demand. So much more is done for London children nowadays with camps etc.'[193]

The Committee also reported that there were ninety-eight enemy air raids over Eastbourne during the war,[194] although the Hospital was 'fortunate to escape serious injury, the chief damage being broken windows.' However, Rose Bunnett, who joined the staff of All Saints in 1938 at the age of sixteen, reported that the men's staircase in the Hospital was hit by machine-gun bullets, although there is no surviving evidence of this.[195] Rose also recalled that in July 1939 there were eighty-two men and 100 women convalescent patients in All Saints, it was the height of their season (April-September). When the Hospital was taken over by the War Office it was on condition that the Sisters stayed to care for civilian casualties, staff salaries being paid by the Government. Patients were advised that they could go home if they wanted to, and in fact there were no convalescent patients at the Hospital during the air raids. A Matron and two resident Medical Officers were brought in (Rose worked as a maid in the Hospital Guest House at first, later looking after the Medical Officers).

During the air raids, according to Rose, those who were mobile took cover in the cellar near the kitchen, spending many nights down there on chairs and camp beds. Sister Ethelburga (Sister Superior) was a 'tower of strength,' especially when Coventry was bombed and the siren sounded all through the night and until the following midday. Rose said that a troop of Canadian soldiers were billeted nearby, and because they particularly loved Sister Ethelburga on one occasion they arranged for three hampers of food to be send to the Sisters. Soldiers marched in the courtyard by the stables and kitchens, there were always two soldiers on duty at the gates, and the staff and patients had to take their passports if they went out of the Hospital

---

[193] Sister Hildegard: 5.

[194] Sources vary – George Humphrey in *Wartime Eastbourne* (Beckett Features, 1989) gives the number of raids as 112, causing 1,106 casualties, of which 174 were fatal, with 1,000 homes seriously damaged and 10,000 slightly damaged. Humphrey thus subtitles his book 'The story of the most raided town in the south-east.' See pp. 7-8

[195] Conversation between the author and Rose Bunnett, a nursing auxiliary at All Saints 1938-1958.

grounds. Lord Haw Haw raised staff morale one day by mentioning All Saints on the radio. 'We have not forgotten the big hospital on the seafront.' The seafront was a no-go area, wrapped in barbed wire, staff and patients had to carry gas masks. One day the sirens went as Rose was trying on shoes in a shop: she had to refer to the list of 'shelters' that everyone had to carry with them (the list included churches, in which there were bowls of apples for the stranded). Prayers were said whenever the sirens sounded. All the staff had to do firewatch duty. Windows were smashed day after day, and were eventually boarded up as replacement was impossible. It was impossible to have Midnight Mass at Christmas because the Chapel couldn't be blacked out.

Various alterations took place in order to accommodate the new casualties. The two patient sitting rooms (St. Anne's and St. Faith's) were used as an operating theatre and for X-ray, the top floor wards were closed (St. Agnes, St. Nicholas and St. Joseph). Sister Edytha was in charge of theatre during the war, and according to Rose, she was as good as any Medical Doctor. There was a big Dispensary on the ground floor at the Hospital, where Sister Edytha made up all the medicines on the men's side.

Casualties weren't the only patients however. In October 2000 Ron Levy wrote an article for the Eastbourne Herald: his birth certificate declared that he had been born at 'All Saints U.D. Eastbourne on 11 November 1939.' His mother had told him, as a young boy, that he was born in a convent hospital at Beachy Head when she was evacuated from London, apparently in one of the top floor wards. It transpires that as part of the war preparations in 1939, St. Mary's Maternity Unit in Eastbourne closed and extra beds were made available at the Maternity Home in Upperton Road. Then on 1st September, 207 cases from London hospitals were 'decanted' to St. Mary's; out of the resulting total of 244 patients, 156 were transferred to All Saints.[196] This, presumably, is how Ron Levy's mother, evacuated from London, came to give birth at All Saints. After a time there were no more civilian casualties; instead, All Saints newly equipped theatres were used for children needing tonsillectomies.

Despite the bombing of Meads Street and other areas near the Hospital on 7 March 1943[197] it appears that none of the original stained glass windows were damaged, unlike at St. Saviour's, where most of the Clayton & Bell windows were lost. This invites speculation that the stained glass windows were boarded up or even temporarily removed.

---

[196] John Surtees (1992) op.cit: 67.
[197] I am grateful to Vera Hodsell for this detail.

XI
The end of an era

The Hospital re-opened for the reception of Adult Patients only on 1st January 1946 and Rose Bunnett reports that there were now new rules and regulations and fewer All Saints Sisters, who were not trained for the new procedures. Charges had to be raised so that Adult patients without a Subscriber's letter would pay £2.10.0 (in 1939 the charge had been £1.5.0). The charge to Hospitals, Friendly and Benevolent Societies for a yearly Bed for Adults only had been fixed at £120 per annum, payable in advance. Annual Subscribers and Life Governors were to pay £6.0.0 for adults (ie. £2.0.0 per week), whilst the rate of subscription remained unchanged at One Guinea.[198]. By 1948 the charge had gone up to 56s per week, and the London County Council had reserved twenty beds, for which they would pay 56s per week whether or not they were occupied. However, between 1946 and 1958 the Hospital took the same number of convalescent patients, 100 women and eighty-two men in the summer season, admitting men on Tuesdays and Fridays, women on Mondays and Thursdays – twenty-four patients at a time.

Most of the patients were mobile, some could go out to the cinemas or to listen to the brass bands on the seafront, but were not allowed out after 9 pm. St. Martha's and St. Joseph's wards on the ground floor were used for the more disabled patients. Sister Mary Christabel looked after the patients over forty years old; the patients under forty, who unlike the older ones, were allowed to smoke, were befriended and read to by Sister Emily Elizabeth. Each morning patients were wheeled along the main drive and out on to the seafront, where they were lined up on the slope above Holywell Retreat to receive two and a half hours of bracing sea air. Rose commented on how much better each of the patients was at the end of their two or three weeks at the Hospital.

During the winter months, the staff did the spring-cleaning, when there were very few, if any, patients. There were sixteen beds in each of the big wards and side wards, four colostomy

---

[198]Notice of fee increase May 1939 & 'Notice of Re-opening,' 13th December 1945, All Saints Convent Archive.

patients, and St. Agnes Ward was now occupied by TB patients (at one point twelve young women between 16-25 came for three months).

Rose, whose uniform in those days consisted of white cap, white overalls just below the knee, black stockings and black shoes, can remember all the staff at this time (the turnover of staff was always very low). Sister Miriam was in charge; she is said to have preferred the men to the women. Sister Bridget ran St. Luke's. The Doctor came to see the women on Fridays and the men on Saturdays. There were two male orderlies and several trained nurses. Sister Lisa Mary was in charge of the kitchen, with Kathleen Cocksedge, Head Cook, and Bessie Howey, from Sunderland, as Assistant Cook, and there were three other girls 'in back.' Local people from Meads also used to help with the washing up.

'Not Under State Control'[199]

In 1948 the Solicitors of the Hospital received a letter from the Ministry of Health stating that the Minister of Health was of the opinion that All Saints Convalescent Hospital was not transferable under the provisions of the National Health Service Act of 1946. The Committee was greatly relieved that the Hospital would be free from Government control, and immediately set about (rather unsuccessfully) reassuring, and restoring support from, Subscribers and Friends by a public advertising campaign.[200] By 1952, the Community was short of novices and not all of Sister Barbara's team could maintain her standards of efficiency. The policy in the past had been to accept full responsibility for all the work: nursing, housekeeping and finance, but finally it was accepted that there was a need for new expertise and specialist training.

In addition it seemed that there was less need of convalescent hospitals than previously (although this is contradicted somewhat by the 1947 Board of Almoners Report previously mentioned) – post-war housing was better, more privacy in homes, radio and television at home. According to Dr. Ian Brown, All Saints incumbent Medical Officer, Sister Barbara had great resilience and devotion, and was very loving and generous: that is to say, some patients paid, others didn't, and the financial situation was not good. (Similarly, Sister Bridget was described by Mr. Gaston, the Hospital's resident engineer, as 'very much in charge,' but she

---

[199] This phrase appeared on the Hospital's headed notepaper between 1948 and 1958.
[200] Minutes of the Hospital Advisory Committee, 26th May 1948.

'never had a thought about the money.')[201] Dr. Brown had the idea to close for convalescents but open for the aged and continue thereby to serve the fundamental principle of All Saints.'

Whilst All Saints Convalescent Hospital was moving into freefall, the All Saints Community transferred their Home for elderly and people with special needs from Finchley to Seaford. The Community had been in Finchley since 1914 but now had to move because of inadequate premises. On 30th June 1953 St. Elizabeth's, Seaford, now housed in what was previously a boys' boarding school, was blessed by the Bishop of Chichester, an occasion attended by four Sisters from All Saints at Eastbourne. The Bishop said that 'the Welfare State could not do for the sick and infirm what Religious in their love and patience did.'[202]

The Home was able to accommodate seventy-eight patients on the spacious ground and first floors, and up to nine Sisters on the second floor. There was also a small private flat for visiting priests and a Chaplain's House, St. Richard's. A local doctor cared for the patients under the new National Health legislation. At this time it was difficult for the Sisters to recruit nurses in Seaford and in 1954 black nurses were brought over from Cape Town, where many All Saints Sisters had worked (1876-c.1945). St. Elizabeth's continued until 1968, by which time the number of Sisters had so diminished that it was necessary to close, transferring resources to St. John's Home adjoining the All Saints Sisters' Convent at Cowley, Oxford.

On 18th November 1957 the Chair of the Trustees had to report to his Committee Members that he had received a letter from the Reverend Mother of the All Saints Sisters that 'owing to the lack of Sisters she felt compelled to withdraw their Services to the Hospital, with very much regret. This decision was received with great concern by all...it was hoped a way would be found to continue the work for convalescents.'[203] In February 1958 the Hospital was put up for sale, and permission given by the Ministry of Housing and Local Government for change of use to a girls' boarding school run by the Roman Catholic La Sainte L'Union Congregation. However, there was strong local pressure for nursing work to be continued at the Hospital, in particular to cater for the elderly sick of Eastbourne and district, for whom there was an acute shortage of accommodation in the area. By the end of 1958 the great work of the Sisters at All

---

[201] Ibid: 124.
[202] Cited in Mayhew, op.cit: 129.
[203] Minutes of All Saints Convalescent Hospital Advisory Committee, 18th November 1957.

Saints Convalescent Hospital, Eastbourne was over – and the Hospital was acquired by the Ministry of Health to continue as a convalescent and geriatric Hospital.[204]

It was perhaps the end of an era in several respects. It has been possible in this book to trace, through the history of All Saints Convalescent Hospital, distinct changes in some of the medical and financial structures of British health care, developments in the history of women's religious communities, and in women's work in general. As we have seen, the issue of work was central to the concerns of women in the latter half of the nineteenth century, and since the First World War and universal women's suffrage there have been many new employment opportunities for women. The opening up of the professions to women, and to married women in particular, meant that women were no longer restricted to the three traditional twentieth century areas of women's labour: teaching, nursing and secretarial work. Just as it had been difficult to recruit nurses for St. Elizabeth's at Seaford in the 1950s, All Saints at Eastbourne was finding it extremely difficult to recruit nurses in the 1960s, such that Members of the Hospital Committee felt it necessary to appeal through the local press for staff and to approach both the Red Cross and St. John's Ambulance for help,[205] despite the establishment of several enterprising schemes during this period, including one whereby young Scandinavian and Finnish women could be brought over to work as auxiliaries and the same time receive tuition in English. Later, under the auspices of the National Health Service, All Saints hosted an Enrolled Nurses Training School (1961) and later a Pupil Nurse Training School (1965-1968).

Despite Peter Anson's assertion, in the 1950s, that 'Wherever the ascetic and mystical impulse exists, which is *natural* to man, there is a tendency to form communities, usually based on poverty and some degree of chastity and obedience. Monasticism, in one form or another, flourishes in environments so diverse that it can only be the expression of a principle inherent in human nature'[206] the numbers of women coming into religious communities had also been diminishing for many years. The conditions that had brought so many women into the Sisterhoods between 1850 and 1900, that is, the desire to help the many who were suffering, the absence of appropriate work in the lives of middle class women, and the powerful spiritual

---

[204] Father Hubert Brasier (father of Shadow Cabinet Minister, Theresa May) was the last Chaplain to the Sisters, and living in South Lodge at the time of the Hospital's closure. The Sisters had at first been reluctant to accept their first married Chaplain.

[205] Minutes of the All Saints Hospital Advisory Committee, 3rd December 1965.

[206] Anson, op.cit: xii.

energy of the Anglo-Catholic revival, were no longer present by the 1950s. There had been a general decline in religious interest; many of the disciplines of convent life were not relaxed until the 1960s and had become increasingly anachronistic; women were encouraged, more than ever in the aftermath of each of the world wars, to be at the centre of domestic life and to become mothers; and the Welfare State now took care of the sick and the poor.

Moreover, as the Sisters of All Saints Convalescent Hospital had long discovered, the task of raising and managing funds for the care of the sick and the poor was an increasingly arduous and complex task, and as we already know about the Sisters, strict financial management wasn't necessarily a priority. From the beginning, the Sisters operated on a principle of optimism, taking the risk of proceeding with their plans and sorting the money out later, illustrated by a statement in the *Eastbourne Gazette*, reporting the opening of the All Saints Chapel in 1874. Talking of new wards, guest rooms, a linen store and enlargement of the refectories, the reporter says: 'The expenses incurred in carrying out these latter additions and improvements have been entered into with *a hope* of their being defrayed by the public.'[207] As we have seen, of the original cost of building the Hospital (£36,000) £10,000 was still outstanding when the Hospital opened.

In the later nineteenth century benefactors were in abundance; during and after the First World War, many patrons were forced to withdraw their support. The Hospital's use as a Military Unit led to a great deal of extra maintenance work, and the costs of labour and materials had risen enormously. Even the Sisters' usual practice of appealing for funds was thwarted by shortage of newsprint and other problems now encountered by the press. In the 1920s the Hospital was forced to sell some of its stocks and shares to raise money for repairs and land facing Meads Street was sold off (over the entire period of the Sisters' work at All Saints Hospital, pieces of the original land were sold to raise money). Even after this the Hospital was running on a deficit for a number of years, and then the Second World War broke out. Although the weekly charges were regularly raised (the charge was doubled between 1938 and 1946) the cost of maintaining the fabric of the building and the quality of care for the patients meant that the number of patients had to be reduced from 125 down to eighty.

Thus from August 1959 the Hospital was re-established as a secular institution, with the renaming of the wards that had so long ago been named after the Saints, Roselands and Devonshire (ground floor), Meads and Holywell for long-stay patients (first floor), and Seaside

---

[207] *Eastbourne Gazette*, 8 July 1874. My emphasis.

and Merlynn for the convalescents (second floor). According to Minutes of the All Saints 'Ad Hoc' Planning Committee, the staff would consist of a Matron and Assistant Matron (housed in South Lodge), ten senior nursing staff (in the Hospital's flats), approximately sixteen nursing and domestic staff (in the old Sisters' wing), five domestic staff (to be housed on the top floor, west), plus the Chaplain and a Dispenser. North Lodge was to be reserved for Mr. Gaston, the long-standing Hospital engineer, the vegetable gardens, glass houses and frames were to be let to a 'reputable firm,' the Sisters' private chapel was to be converted to a sitting room, and the apple store be converted into a mortuary.[208] St. Luke's was sold and demolished, its patients transferred to All Saints Hospital, and by 1961 the Hospital – now one of seven hospitals administered by the Eastbourne and District Hospital Management Committee - was able to accommodate 101 long-stay patients and fifty-one convalescents.[209]

On 19th July 1969, exactly 100 years after its inauguration, a new three-ward extension to the Hospital was opened, fittingly, by the current Duke of Devonshire, an occasion attended by the Mother Superior and Sisters of the All Saints Community. In 1984 the Saints' Club opened, providing social and recreational facilities for patients and members of the community; and in 1997 the Day Hospital that was previously at the Princess Alice Hospital, Eastbourne (demolished 1997) moved to All Saints - the Princess Alice Unit - providing a day service for elderly patients undergoing rehabilitation. Services currently available include physiotherapy, occupational therapy, chiropody and speech therapy.

In more recent years the Hospital has been threatened on several occasions with closure. In 1991 it was reported that All Saints would, with the District General Hospital and Princess Alice Hospital, move out of the National Health Service into the control of an independent NHS trust (Eastbourne Hospitals NHS Trust), then All Saints would be sold off to pay for the refurbishment of the Princess Alice Hospital for the rehabilitation and long-term care of the elderly.[210] In 1992 it was reported that both the Princess Alice and All Saints would be replaced, respectively by nursing homes and a new hospital possibly on the site of the Princess Alice Hospital.[211]

---

[208] <u>Minutes of the All Saints 'Ad Hoc' Planning Committee</u>, April 1959-March 1960.

[209] Giddey, op.cit: 20-22.

[210] *Eastbourne Herald*, 9th November 1991.

[211] *Eastbourne Herald*: 21st November 1992.

Again in 1995 a plan was made to move All Saints staff and facilities to the more central District General Hospital by 1997.[212] By April that same year, however, the proposed development of the All Saints site (to be converted into thirty-three flats, thirty-five garages and fifteen parking spaces) was strongly resisted by the Meads Community Association, and a decision on the development was deferred.[213] Then in 2000 staff at All Saints were told of the decision to shut the Hospital early in 2003, transferring some patients to the District General Hospital, Eastbourne and other accommodation, and developing new services in the community. At the time of writing, the Hospital is due to close in 2004 or 2005. The Hospital still provides a full rehabilitation service for elderly patients.

---

[212]*Eastbourne Herald*: 18th February 1995.
[213]*Eastbourne Herald*: 22nd April 1995.

XII
'All Gothic, with an apsed Chapel'[214]

'On Festivals we had lovely Processions of Sisters before Vespers, simply
right up the spacious Chapel and round by the little Cloister to
the stairs leading to the Tribune which was where
we Sisters sang or recited our Offices.[215]

Finally we come to the Hospital's *pièce de résistance*, the Chapel, Henry Woodyer's masterpiece, the one aspect of Harriet Brownlow Byron's great vision that remains much as she first saw it.

To reach the Chapel from the Hospital's reception area, you must first descend into a narrow cloister, becoming aware of the light given by a procession of silver-yellow stamped-quarried glass windows.[216] The light falls on to the terracotta, black and white diapered quarry tiles beneath your feet, and you are struck by the repetition of pattern as you walk along. More than struck – you are *propelled* by the repetition, beginning to hurry, in growing anticipation. At the end of the passage on the right is a stone staircase leading up to the Tribune, the gallery above the Chapel where, according to the strict rule of worship central to monastic life, the Sisters recited their Hours. On the left, before you enter the Chapel, you catch the eye of the Foundress Mother, Harriet Brownlow Byron, with her steady gaze and hint of self-irony. And then, with one more step, you're through the tall middle-pointed oak door with its unique strap hinge and inside the Chapel.

There is something so coherent, so absolute about this Chapel that one experiences an intense blow. First you experience what Canon Denys Giddey has called the 'cumulative power of prayer,'[217] but which may equally be a profound aesthetic experience: the absolute harmony

---

[214] This is the cursory entry in Ian Nairn & Nikolaus Pevsner (1973) *The Buildings of England: Sussex*, Penguin: 488.
[215] S. Caroline Mary, cited in Mumm (2001): 26.
[216] This is an example of the way Woodyer used designs from the medieval period. The manufacturer of these stained glass windows is Hardman Powell (see below). Hung on the cloister walls are several watercolours of the Hospital and Chapel painted by Colin Fairchild (2001).
[217] In conversation with the author, April 2002. Canon Giddey is also the author of *The Story of All Saints Hospital, Eastbourne* (op.cit).

that results from the exquisite choice and combination of materials, dimension and scale, shape, texture, light and colour. Perhaps it is both experiences, powerfully combined.

Once you have recovered from that initial impact, your eye is drawn down the centre aisle towards the east windows - tall, narrow lancet windows - and you renew your understanding of the word 'illumination.' Everything in the Chapel leads the eye to the east windows and the altar. You experience, rather than merely see, the stained glass windows either side of the Chapel, the repeated arches, the clusters of pillars, the diapered quarry floor tiles down the centre aisle which metamorphose into insistent ceramic triangles and stars, their colours intensifying with each of the seven steps to the altar. You notice the terracotta medallions of the sacred monogram repeated at different heights against the polychrome bands of red brickwork and white stonework. You are apprehended by the blue Devon stone and the gloss-yellow stripes across the brickwork as you move away from the altar, past the shimmer of the marble pillars and the dryness of the altar arches. Your eye searches left and right for more colour: ruby, blood, crimson, purple, soon finding the silver and lemon-gold of the nimbus over the head of St. Charles in the windows of the Chapel of the Blessed Sacrament.

Eventually, depending on the brightness of the day, something else comes into your vision: the groined wooden ceiling above the altar: *fleur-de-lis*, ribbons of muted blue and green, and the nimbus-encircled heads of the twelve apostles: '*Simon (Peter), and his brother Andrew; James, the son of Zebedee, and John his brother; Philip, and Bartholomew; Thomas, and Matthew the publican; James the son of Alphaeus, and Lebbaeus, whose surname was Thaddeus; Simon the Canaanite, and Judas Iscariot…Heal the sick, cleanse the lepers, raise the dead, cast out devils: freely he have received, freely give.*'[218]

That you cannot see exactly what is high above you is precisely the point: one is cognizant that there is beauty above one's head, there is devotion, there is sustenance, but we can only glimpse, and not imagine that we can know it whilst on earth.[219]

Design and construction

Like the Hospital, All Saints Chapel is built on an east-west axis, allowing the sea light to flood through the east windows. The Chapel is 111ft long, 31ft 6in wide, and 58ft high. One thinks

---

[218] Matthew: 10,1-8.
[219] In fact, painted and gilt in foliage with heads of the Apostles.

immediately of an ark: the Church as ark, leading the congregation through time.[220] Both the Hospital and the Chapel, sailing above the sea, above the town, have this ark-like quality. The plain brick exterior is of a lighter hue than that of the Hospital, and despite the idiosyncratic series of plate tracery designs and the delicate stone trellis work around the top of the east windows, one does not immediately suspect that the interior of the Chapel will be so beautiful.

The Chapel is of collegiate style with a continuous roof over nave and sanctuary. Inside, as described by the *Eastbourne Gazette* just after the Chapel's opening, the **nave** consists of eight bays between clusters of moulded stone columns, the centre shafts of which carry the principals of the roof. From side shafts spring arches on which rest moulded roof plates. The polygonal apse and the two bays next to it are ceiled with wooden groining, which has been richly painted and gilt in foliage, with the heads of the Apostles in the several groine spaces.[221] The Chapel is considered Woodyer's

'most Butterfieldian style with rich polychrome of red and black brick, prominent horizontal stripes of white stone and amber and black tile, terracotta medallions and polished marble colonnettes. The horizontal banding is balanced by the vertical lines of attached stone columns and arches framing each window and forming an arcade down each side of the chapel. At the west end five single lancet windows are arranged in a stepped pattern under the gable end, whilst below is a high timber gallery supported on marble columns.'[222]

The builders for Woodyer's design were once again Wheelers of Reading, the heating and water supply were by Messrs. Addis of London, the carving by Nicholls of London and the metalwork was by Filmer and Mason of Guildford. One can imagine the skilled labour

---

[220] 'Churches express time – but in terms of space.' Margaret Visser (2002) *The Geometry of Love: Space, Time, Mystery and Meaning in an Ordinary Church*, Penguin: 15.
[221] *Eastbourne Gazette*, 8th July 1874.
[222] Elliott & Pritchard, op.cit: 240.

contained in the precise placing and pointing of every brick, of the delicate curves of the clustered pillars: as John Ruskin says, 'One of the most marked distinctions between one artist and another, in the point of skill, will be found in their relative delicacy of perception of rounded surface...'[223] The contrast between the different types of labour, the tension between the plain and the extremely ornate, between the mass and the line – these are things that we are unconsciously aware of, things that make, through tiny, discrete movements in our perception, an impact on our senses.

The **sanctuary** is on seven levels, symbolising the seven sacraments. The altar steps are made from Devon marble and laid with elaborate geometric patterns of encaustic tiles manufactured by Minton in brick red, dark green, white, black, blue grey, then up a step into pale green, red, white, black and grey, then on the next level, blue, green, no black.[224] The repeated shapes in the floor pattern – pentagons, octagons, triangles, circles, stars all have particular symbolic significance in the Gothic tradition: for example, circle is an emblem of Heaven and Eternity, the equilateral triangle (represented in the many trefoils in the plate tracery and the balustrades of the Hospital's grand staircases) is a symbol of the Holy Trinity, and is also sometimes represented by three circles; the octagon symbolizes regeneration.[225] At the edges of the altar steps are floral corner tiles from designs by Pugin.

The **high altar** is made from oak, and has been moved a little away from its original position against the wall. The altar is unusually wide and long, very dignified by the standards of the time, and in accordance with the Anglo-Catholic tradition in which the altar must be visible at once, unlike the high-pewed, high-pulpit churches of the past. Tractarian churches are identifiable by their open altars, whilst many Commissioners' churches have obscuring features (rails, for example, concealing part of the altar; the present rails in the Chapel are a later addition).[226] The width of the High Altar is significant to one's experience of the whole Chapel.

---

[223] John Ruskin, (1849) *The Seven Lamps of Architecture,* George Allen (1904 edition): 165.

[224] *Encaustic:* from the Greek meaning 'burnt in'. Minton's encaustic tiles were made in moulds at the bottom of which was a raised design. Herbert Minton was a second generation pottery manufacturer; he started making encaustic floor tiles, many of them, such as those in the Palace of Westminster, to Pugin's designs. Minton revived and adapted the medieval techniques.

[225] See A.Welby Pugin (1858), *Glossary of Ecclesiastial Ornament and Costume,* Bernard Quaritch.

[226] The author is grateful to Dr. A. Wakely, Administrator of All Saints Convent at Oxford, for this information.

The front of the High Altar is decorated with paintings of nine saints, each in a trefoil-headed niche. There is evidence of a correspondence between the Mother Superior and the Munich Ecclesiastical Art and Stained Glass Establishment at 37 Conduit Street, London about the Saints represented in the Altar Table, suggesting that the reredos and the Altar Table (and, one might speculate, the German windows) were all commissioned through this Establishment. The Munich Establishment state that the Saints represented in the Altar Table are, from the left, St. Alban, St. Etheldreda,, St. Andrew and St. Bridget; in the centre, St. Vincent de Paul, then to the right, St. Barbara, St. Augustine and, St. Jane Frances de Chantal, and St. George. The red damask altar curtains were given in 1964 by the All Saints Community. The crucifix and the altar candlesticks are from designs by Pugin.

The ornamental screen behind the High Altar, the **reredos**, is a triptych showing Christ in Glory surrounded by archangels and saints, the four archangels, the emblems of the four evangelists, the Blessed Mother on the right and St. Mary Magdalene on the left. Among the other figures are St. Peter, St. Andrew, St. John the Baptist, St. Lawrence, St. Agnes, St. Catherine, St. Edward, St. Joseph, St. Cecilia, St. Stephen, St. Ursula and St. Helen.[227]

The reredos was painted by Julius Frank (1826-c.1908) of Munich, a well-known portrait painter of the time, whose only other known English ecclesiastical commission is his decorative work in Stoneyhurst Roman Catholic College in Preston in or around 1858. The reredos, which was not complete until after the Chapel opened, was an 'offering to the hospital for benefits received from it.'[228] It was restored and floodlit in 1964. Behind and surrounding the reredos there are exceptionally rare carved window **mullions**, featuring finely carved stone figures of Saints, a series of angels climbing as if toward Heaven, and statues of angels in canopied niches, silhouetted by the eastern light behind them.

To the left of the high altar is a brass memorial plaque bearing the name of Reverend William Upton Richards, Mother Foundress's great inspiration, dated 1873. It is to Reverend Upton Richards that the east windows are dedicated.

On the north side of the chancel there is a **squint** (*hagioscope*), an oblique opening through the wall to allow sight lines between the high altar and the aisle to be established. They usually occur, though not in this Chapel, on either side of the chancel arch. This would have required enormous ingenuity and skill in the carving.

---

[227] Original letter 2nd October 1874, in All Saints Convent Archives.
[228] According to the *Eastbourne Gazette*, 8th July 1874.

The **Chapel of the Blessed Sacrament** and the second altar were added to the north of the High Altar in memory of the first Sister Superior at Eastbourne, Sister Anne, who died in1918, having given nearly fifty years of her working life to the Hospital.

The **lectern** is a brass eagle. Pugin states that the eagle is 'appropriated to St. John, for as that bird faces the sun, so this Prince of the Evangelists soars to contemplate the great mystery of Christ's Divinity.'[229]

Imagine playing Bach in the small north transept of this Chapel, in the darkness: this is what Canon Giddey used to do, on the present **organ**, built by J. Walker & Sons and installed in 1904, before which there was a harmonium. The organ, which is still played, was overhauled in 1965, following painstaking and lengthy fundraising by Canon Giddey and the Friends of All Saints Hospital. There have been many public organ recitals here over the years and concerts such as the recent Mozart Requiem, which demonstrate the exceptional quality of the acoustic in the Chapel.

At the west end of the Chapel stands the **font**, opposite the main door. It is a leaded bowl of red marble supported by emblems of the four Evangelists in alabaster on a black marble base, which is inscribed with the words 'Except a man be born again he cannot see the Kingdom of God' (St. John 3,3). The font cover, lifted by a compensated weight system, has an arched wrought-iron crown decorated with bats' wings, and at the top, an orb, surmounted by a cross, bearing the words 'In the Name of the Father, the Son and the Holy Ghost.' Along the back of the Chapel is a row of twelve oak **choirstalls** each with a misericord.[230] Each of the several hundred chairs along the main aisles is furnished with a new woven seat squab, the result of an extraordinary Millennium project organised by Geraldine Griffiths and involving volunteer weavers from every continent.

It was Mother Foundress's idea to have 'a **tribune** at the west end of the Chapel where [the Sisters] could say the Divine Office affront.'[231] The screened gallery is made of oak and carried by Devonshire marble columns, the same material being used for the staircase up to the Tribune and at the east end of the Chapel. In one of the three stained glass windows in the Tribune is a representation, unusual for the time, of the Sacred Heart, a Roman- rather than Anglo-Catholic devotion.

---

[229] Pugin, op.cit: 115.

[230] The ledge under a hinged seat in a choir stall, giving support to someone when the seat is folded up.

[231] Sister Hildegard, op.cit: 3.

Beneath the apse is a small **crypt**, where, it is said, any Sister who died at All Saints was laid out. The surprise of this crypt is a massive stone cross, part window mullion, part foundation stone perhaps, and more rock than carving. One thinks of St. Peter ('Peter', from the Greek *petros*, which means 'rock'): *'Unto you therefore which believe he is precious: but unto them which be disobedient, the stone which the builders disallowed, the same is made the head of the corner. / And a stone of stumbling, and a rock of offence, even to them which stumble at the word.'*[232] It is a feature that has been described by architect Richard Crook as way before its time,[233] and one that quietly reveals to us a little more about Henry Woodyer.

St. Peter, detail from Chapel window

---

[232] 1 Peter 2, 7-8.
[233] In conversation with the author, September 2002.

'I hope the glass will be rich and deep, the chapel is hungry for it.' Henry Wooder[234]

The windows of the Chapel are one of its special features - indeed, the experience of the Chapel is given mainly by the quality of light and colour, achieved both by the placing and the design of the stained and painted glass windows. Their study affords the opportunity to consider a little of the development of stained glass manufacture, and something of Woodyer's aesthetic and religious sensibilities, as well as further aspects of the Victorian Gothic tradition. The Gothic Revivalists believed in apostolic descent as understood in the medieval period, and this was represented in their stained glass. The Crucifixion is omnipresent, often in the east window of a church or chapel, as is the whole hierarchy of angels *(in whom we can trust)*, so important to Pugin.

The windows in the nave and apse are unusually tall, with Geometrical tracery at the top, and all except two have two lights (the others have three). The three windows at the east end have gables rising through the roof eaves, a device which Woodyer also employed at Clewer. The apse windows and thirteen of the windows in the nave and in the Tribune were designed by Hardman Powell, and four by the Munich firm, George Mayer, or possibly another Munich firm; those depicting the Saints in the Chapel of the Blessed Sacrament and in front of the vestry, are by Mayer. Two windows, to the right and the left of the apse, are simple stamped-quarried. The Hardman windows were put in between 1874 and 1885, under Woodyer's vigilant eye, whereas the German windows may be later (up to 1888).

Hardman & Co. was founded in 1838 after Pugin had persuaded John Hardman to abandon his button-making business to manufacture church and plate fittings under Pugin's artistic directorship. The company's glasswork was displayed in the Great Exhibition of 1851 and was described by The Ecclesiologist as 'a class apart.' After Hardman's death in 1852, his son-in-law John Hardman Powell, became artistic head of the company, and developed a working relationship with Woodyer that was to last for nearly forty years. Hardman Powell ran one of about twelve large glass firms amidst a proliferation of small firms, between them supplying about 80,000 windows to the church building industry here and abroad during the Victorian period. Such was the intensity of critical reception for stained glass that windows new in the

---

[234] Woodyer to Hardman Powell, 11 March 1876,cited in Elliott & Pritchard, op.cit: 115.
[235] Cited in Martin Harrison (1980) *Victorian Stained Glass*, Barrie & Jenkins: 24.
[236] Harrison, op.cit: 10.

1840s and 1850s had become unacceptable by the 1870s and 1880s. During this grand period of glass manufacture in England, there was also serious competition from Germany, France, Italy and Belgium. In the early 1870s the Munich firm of Mayer & Co. was doing enough business in Britain to justify opening an office in London.

The collaboration between Woodyer and Hardman Powell was a fortuitous one: Woodyer wanted stained glass with 'good preaching' windows and rich, deep colour.'[237] Hardman Powell had trained with Pugin, studying the medieval glass in Chartres and Beauvais Cathedrals, working in Pugin's Ramsgate Studio of Christian Art, and with William Butterfield, in whose office Woodyer had trained.[238] Hardman Powell, like rival firms such as Clayton & Bell, and Wailes, used methods of glass manufacture based on those of the medieval period, and between them, the architect and artist produced glass informed by ideas about the 'mystery of light' that had been crucial to theologians and thinkers of medieval times.[239]

Hardman Powell was interested in the way that colours responded differently to northern or southern exposure and worked with the glazier on the choice of colour hue. Woodyer was similarly exacting, being concerned with the precise degree of light appropriate to a particular chapel or church, and favouring rich colours that glowed when lit by the sun. The colour choices made by Woodyer were based on his interpretation of the role of light in religious doctrine and imagery: green represented renewal; red, the divine; blue, peace; and gold, eternal arrival. Light is heavenly matter; glass captures the light. The (revived) medieval method of glass manufacture made the glass glisten, the result of bubbles and unevenness in the metal content, which stopped the light and made it radiate. Describing his and Hardman Powell's glass at his church St. Michael in Tenbury Wells, Woodyer wrote that 'It has all that beautiful complexity and glitter for which the old glass is remarkable.'[240]

In the Hardman windows, the human figures are characterised by long necks, classical faces, delicate hands and fingers, and mystery in the faces of the angels. He preferred 'complex scenes peopled with his distinctive, elongated, Gothic S-shaped figures, inspired…by Sienese

---

[237] Woodyer to Hardman, 1st October 1856, cited by Shepheard in Elliott & Pritchard, op.cit: 109.

[238] Butterfield and Powell argued, however, and didn't work together at all between 1860 and 1872. Woodyer was Powell's first client after this rift.

[239] Elliott & Pritchard, op.cit: 109.

[240] Ibid: 117. John Ruskin was also interested in this mysterious quality of light: he would sit and be engulfed by the light (representing the soul or spirit), by the balance given by the composition of stained windows: the re-ordering of chaos into compositional form.

painters…'[241] The sweep of the shapes invites us to enter and follow. Another Hardman feature is the recognition of Christ's pastoral role among the people, and he wove into his glass, paintings of local children and local scenes. Powell's work is also known for its sensitivity of line and the placing of the leads.

The German (Mayer) windows in the Chapel are much more romantic; they have a pre-Raphaelite, theatrical and literal quality: huge soulful eyes, rich, dark colours, a kind of reckless voluptuousness. It is precisely these characteristics that have, in the past, caused them to be despised. Woodyer said, for example, that Mayer's glass was wretched, that it would be 'neither old in quality or spirit' and didn't share his ideas about the use and function of the saddle bars. By comparison, the Hardman Powell windows are more serious, designed for contemplation rather than sensation.

It was common practice to dedicate windows to loved ones or to those who had been inspirational to one's work. In All Saints Chapel, the three apse windows are dedicated to Harriet Brownlow Byron's mentor and co-founder, Reverend William Upton Richards; and it is apparent from the Powell/Hardman correspondence that Mother Foundress herself commissioned one of the windows.[242]

The Opening of the Chapel

Initially, worship took place in a temporary chapel 'at the top of the Hospital and there was no lift, so the infirm could not get to the Chapel. Brother Hall [later to become the Bishop of Vermont] …would carry…crippled boys on his back up the stairs to the Chapel.'[243] When the resident Chaplain was away the Sisters often had to go without Service, but those who were able used to walk across the corn fields to St. Saviour's Church in South Street, which was apparently the only church in Eastbourne where early 'celebrations' were held, and even then, only on Sundays and holidays.[244]

At the Blessing of the Chapel 4th July 1874 Dr. Durnford, Bishop of Chichester, said that the Sisters were 'rich only in self-denial, in self-sacrifice, in love.'[245] The subject of his discourse was

---

[241] Harrison, op.cit: 27.

[242] There are also other dedications in the Chapel: for example, a plaque in memory of Lady Henrietta Louisa Ogilvy, who died 26th August 1888, and the painting of the Madonna and Child is dedicated to Paul Frederick Tidman, CMG, and his wife Frances.

[243] Sister Catherine Williams, in Mumm (2001): 61.

taken from the second verse, fifth chapter of the Gospel of St. John:

"Now there is at Jerusalem, by the Sheep Market, a pool which is called in the Hebrew tongue Bethesda, having five porches." His Lordship said the meaning of the word Bethesda was house of mercy, but he thought this name referred not so much to the visit of the angel to the water as the existence of the porches…He hoped that among the signs of quickened life in the present day the love of the sick would be eminent….this Bethesda [All Saints]….had, however, a higher aspect than that of succouring the body; it was a house of refuge and mercy for the soul…This chapel, said his lordship, was exceedingly magnificent; it was a place worthy of dedication to God, and may they who worship in it feel Him near and dear to them. May we and they now and ever know and feel that this is none other than the house of God, the very gate of heaven.' [246]

All Saints Hospital Chapel continues to be 'a house of refuge and mercy for the soul'. Staff and patients still take nourishment from the Chapel's beauty and silence. Services, weddings, baptisms and concerts continue to take place. Anna Menchon cleans the Chapel, polishing with a duster in each hand and these days employing an electric floor polisher - and the Chapel still glistens with human labour and love.

Detail of the Chapel floor

[244] St. Saviour's has been is described by Victorian historian and architect, Richard Crook, as competing with All Saints Hospital Chapel as the other 'most important example of Victorian architecture in the town.' R. Crook (undated) *A Peep at Victorian Eastbourne.*
[245] In Mayhew, op.cit: 120.
[246] *Eastbourne Gazette*, 8th July 1874.

Leaving [a church] is as momentous as going in…' [247]

At the 150th Anniversary of the Society of the All Saints Sisters of the Poor at All Saints, Margaret Street on 20 October 2001, The Most Reverend David Hope, Archbishop of York remarked on some of the changes that have taken place in the ways of the Sisterhood since those Victorian days:

'…just as it has had to move on in other ways the Society has also had to move on in its understanding of the Religious Life; coming to understand just how diminishing had been that old idea that the giving of self was only to be achieved by the suppression of self; and learning instead that self-giving – that generous, profligate, abandoned self-giving reflective of the generous, profligate, abandoned self-giving which is in the very heart of God…there has been from the very beginning – and true to the monastic ideal from the very earliest of days – *something both of provisionality and of risk about the Society* – its style and way of life. It has been a sign of protest and of contradiction to the Church and to the world -'[248]

The extraordinary work, so often in adversity, of the All Saints Sisters continues materially, no longer in Margaret Street, London, but in Oxford: Helen House and Douglas House Hospices for Children and Young People, St. John's Home, a residential home for the elderly, and the Porch Steppin' Stone Centre; and in their Community in Baltimore, USA. Their work also continues in spirit, and All Saints Convalescent Hospital embodies that spirit. The love, self-sacrifice, devotion and sheer hard labour of staff, volunteers and Friends, are palpable in this Hospital.

'Sister Caroline Mary watched over Sister for 4 days: '*a lovely corpse…as she lay dead in her coffin, a wonderful beauty came on her perfectly reposeful face, and day to day seemed to increase.*'[249]

Let us watch over All Saints, let its beauty increase.

---

[247] Margaret Visser (2002) *The Geometry of Love: Space, Time, Mystery and Meaning in an Ordinary Church*, Penguin: 27.
[248] Printed in *All Saints Parish Paper,* December 2001: 8-9, my emphasis.
[249] S. Caroline Mary, in Mumm (1999): 55.